Chic & Slim
Armoire
Boudoir
Cuisine
& Savvy

Success Techniques for Wardrobe Relaxation
Food & Smart Thinking

Anne Barone

A Chic & Slim Book

Chic & Slim ARMOIRE BOUDOIR CUISINE & SAVVY:
Success Techniques For Wardrobe Relaxation Food & Smart Thinking
Anne Barone

A Chic & Slim Book | The Anne Barone Company
http://www.annebarone.com
Second Edition

Book Cover & Design: Anne Barone
Eiffel Tower Design: Joyce Wells GriggsArt
Cover Image: Copyright © Cindy Hughes/*Shutterstock.com*
Teapot Image: © WC Fonts (*wcfonts.com*) Avignon and Nantes, France
Cover & Heading Typography: Biographer Copyright © Sudtipos

ISBN Print: 978-1-937066-20-8
ISBN Kindle: 978-1-937066-21-5

Disclaimer Notice to Readers: This book is intended as philosophy
and general reference only. It is not a substitute for medical advice or
treatment. Every individual's problems with excess weight are unique
and complex. You should consult your physician for guidance on any
medical condition or health issue and to make certain any products or
treatments you use are right and safe for you. The author and publisher
disclaim any responsibility for any liability, loss or risk incurred directly
or indirectly from the use or application of any of the contents of
this publication or from any of the materials, services or products
mentioned in the contents of this book or in supplemental materials
published on the supporting website *annebarone.com*.

Contents

Dedicated to

All Who Wish To Be Chic & Slim
à la française

Bonjour!

We have long been learning delicious, life-enhancing lessons from the French. The legendary cooking authority Julia Child insisted that anyone anywhere could learn to cook in the French manner—if they had the right instruction.

Cooking in the French manner was simply a matter of technique, Julia Child said. The exact ingredients did not make much difference. In her books and television series she instructed us in those techniques needed to master the art of French cooking.

What is true for the art of French cooking is equally true for the French arts of chic personal style and staying slim.

With the right instruction, any woman anywhere can look chic and stay slim in the French manner. (Men can use the basic philosophy to become attractively dressed and lean.) It is simply a matter of technique. The exact clothes and the exact foods do not make much difference. Choose the clothes and foods that fit your budget and your personal style. The secrets to your success are the techniques.

Chic & Slim *Armoire Boudoir Cuisine & Savvy* is designed to teach you simple and quick French-inspired techniques of wardrobe choice and organization, of creating a place for serene relaxation, of organizing your kitchen and pantry, and French-styled smart thinking—so that you can look chic and stay slim *à la française*.

In this book, you will learn five comprehensive techniques: the four mentioned above, plus a bonus technique on the French art of being blasé. Along with these techniques, I list resources so that you can achieve even more spectacular chic and slim success.

Be chic, stay slim,
Anne Barone

About This 2nd Edition

Chic French Women are always making refinements and improvements to their personal style. When they find a new and useful technique that helps them stay healthy and slim, they adopt that innovation. Likewise, this Second Edition of *Chic & Slim Armoire Boudoir Cuisine & Savvy* has been refined from the original published almost a decade ago. Material no longer useful has been deleted or updated.

Should you start at the beginning and work through to the end? Not with this book. *ABC&S* is designed for flexibility. Begin with the section of your greatest interest or need.

My fervent aim writing this book is to give you lifestyle guidelines so that you can be chic and slim with minimal effort—leaving you the maximum amount of time to pursue your goals and enjoy life's pleasures.

Success Strategies

Simple and Quick Chic & Slim

    Simple and quick. Minimize the effort and time to arrive at the maximum *Chic & Slim* success. *Armoire Boudoir Cuisine & Savvy* aims to give you the easiest techniques for perfecting your chic and insuring your slim. Here are some suggestions for using this book.

    Chic & Slim books have been around since 1997. Some of you now are pros at Anne Barone's system for dressing chic and staying slim *à la française*. Each of you is unique. You represent a variety of geographic, economic and cultural backgrounds. You range in age from teens to octogenarians. Inevitably, not all information will be useful to all of you. Use what seems applicable for your situation for your lifestyle today. Ignore the rest.

    If something makes you uncomfortable, or if it is against your value system, you will likely have success even if you do not incorporate that particular practice into your personal version of *Chic & Slim*. An example of what I am talking about: A number of years ago I received a letter from a woman who had bought the *Chic & Slim* books. She informed me that she was a good Christian woman and it was against her religious beliefs to flirt like a French woman. But she had adopted a number of the other French techniques suggested in the books. As a result she had achieved a most satisfactory weight loss. Her personal style had become much more chic.

    The first technique in this book concerns organizing a small, chic wardrobe based on those that serve French women so well. With one memorable American exception, every woman of truly chic style of any nationality that I have known has maintained an organized closet.

You cannot organize well until you get rid of the excess and the clutter. So I begin the Armoire chapter with the clean-out and organize process. Not the most exciting topic. But necessary.

Because the concept was presented in previous *Chic & Slim* writings, some of you have long ago *been there, done that*. If you find the first part of Armoire boring, skip on over a couple of pages. Or you can read on feeling very superior that you have already mastered that part of the *Chic & Slim* lifestyle.

As I note in the Armoire technique text, I have received much email from *Chic & Slim* Women testifying to the benefits they found from paring down their wardrobes. Below is one. I think it is always useful for you, especially you who are new to *Chic & Slim,* to see how others have put the French philosophy to use.

Dear Anne,

I ordered and received your three books last January, and have been 'Chic & Slim'-ing ever since. I have never looked and felt better. Everyone who knows me notices the difference! My home is decluttered and my wardrobe is pared down to good quality, timeless basics that fit me well and make me feel fabulous. Learning to eat smaller portions (of foods I love, bien sur) has made me feel very elegant and chic, and I've slimmed down to my goal weight. I will be turning 30 this week (not that 30 is old, but it's definitely one of those 'milestone' ages where a woman wants to feel she is on the right track, and often an age where women start to 'slack off' on maintaining their appearance.) Thanks to your books, I have re-discovered how much fun it is to be feminine, and I feel healthy, organized, beautiful, and optimistic about getting older and wiser. It is sad and true that being overweight wrecks women's lives, and it was certainly wrecking mine. Your message to women is very inspiring and very important, mille mercis!

Sincerely, Elisa

For those of you who need encouragement for tackling the job of cleaning out and organizing your wardrobe, I will tell you a true story. Recently, at the home of a friend, while she made a trip to the supermarket for food shopping, a man broke the lock on her back door and broke into her house.

When she arrived back home with her groceries, he was in her bedroom in the process of looking for valuables to steal. She heard him and ran out the front door for help. He ran out the back door with her laptop and her new bottle of expensive perfume. In the process of the burglary, the thief scattered the entire contents of her lingerie drawer on the floor of her bedroom. She was embarrassed at the idea of all those personal items being seen by the policemen that arrived, but the investigating officers would not permit her to touch any of the items while they collected the evidence of the crime. Because many women hide their jewelry in their lingerie drawers, it is common for thieves to dump drawers in the floor as a quick way to search for items to steal.

So think about this: If there were several male police officers in your bedroom and all your underpants, bras, slips, and other lingerie were scattered on the carpet, would you wish that you had perhaps mended or discarded some of those personal items?

In the techniques in this book I provide what can be classified as consumer information. There is a reason.

Since I established the *Chic & Slim* website in 1997, I have become familiar with the type of questions I receive asking for additional information on topics about which I have written in the *Chic & Slim* books or in website postings. A great many of these questions ask for names of brands and products and where to purchase them. Your time and your money are important. My aim is to give you information that can save you both.

Be assured that I receive no financial benefit from providing this information. I purchase all the items I write about with the exception of a few that have been gifts from family or friends.

By the way, one of the reasons there has never been advertising on the *Chic & Slim* website is that this leaves me free to give my honest opinion about the products that I review.

⌑ Some of you will benefit in your *Chic & Slim* efforts if you adopt a more relaxed attitude. American women often do have a habit of taking themselves far too seriously. The following email comments on that point. You will better understand if you read the comment in the context of the whole email. Also a number of the points she raises are discussed in this book.

> Hello Anne,
>
> I wanted to thank you (as everyone else does!) for your wonderful book. I ordered the original Chic and Slim off of Amazon on a whim, and just ordered the other two tonight. I really loved it. Your observations and advice really fit in with a larger theme everyone is seeing now - simplicity, priorities, etc. It is just more fun your way! :)
>
> I also have always felt something of a conflict internally between wanting to be feminine and sexy, and still independent and what I formerly referred to as a "feminist" (who knows what that means anymore!). Reading your book helped me reconcile the two, and is making it easier to make them meet (if that makes any sense).
>
> I think American women most definitely suffer not only from a "martyr" syndrome, but just take themselves too seriously overall. We are also raised (as you mentioned) with a double standard regarding appearance and sexiness, which wreaks havoc with our developing psyches. I mean, I just turned 29 and am just starting to come to terms with some of these issues.
>
> Psychologist, sociologist - or not - I think you have some very valid points about our society. Best of all, you give practical suggestions for us to try, which many people don't. Everyone likes to point out the problems, but not many have solutions. So thank you.
>
> Take care,
>
> Erika

ᥴᥣᦞ Mindset can make a big difference in how useful the this book is for you. The following email addresses this point.

Dear Anne,

I recently ordered all three of your books and have to tell you that I've enjoyed them immensely. In fact, I read all three within a 24-hour period and have been re-reading them more slowly since then. I have found your advice very sensible and helpful; it came along at just the right time for me. Since having two children, I have struggled with a weight-gain of twenty-five pounds and gone on several diets. I always managed to stay on them for awhile, but then I'd get frustrated at the "slow" results and old habits would begin creeping back, along with the weight I'd lost. Finally, fed up, I decided that I was never going to go on another diet. Instead, any change to my lifestyle that I made would have to receive a positive answer to the question, "Am I willing to do this for the rest of my life if I never lose a pound?" (Being a little older and starting to become less concerned about whether or not I look like a model helped.)

Then I happened across your books on amazon and became intrigued after reading the reviews. That was about a month ago. Using the criteria I mentioned above, I decided to make the following changes: I would try eating continental style for the most part (although when challenged with some foods, I still resort to my right hand) in order to slow down my eating. I would take smaller bites and chew them longer than was my habit. I decided not to cut snacking out entirely, but decided that if I was hungry between meals, I would stick with fruit or a Triscuit or two with a little peanut butter or cheese. I would throw out guilt. If I ate something indulgent one day I would simply enjoy the pleasure of that food and then be conscious of compensating for the next day or two with extra vegetables, more water, etc. I decided that I was going to concentrate on the process rather than on results. I was determined not to get into my old habit of weighing myself several times a week. I chose to view these changes as a way of taking care of myself, being good to myself. Well, I stuck with my determination regarding the scale. However, I finally got curious when I noticed that my pants were a bit looser around the waistband, even straight out of the dryer. It turns out that in the last month, without ever feeling like I've been on a diet, I've lost six pounds. That's about the same results I'd have gotten with any of the diets I've been on in the past, but this time, I have an entirely different mindset and it is making all the difference. Diets were like punishment. With this, I feel that I am making mindful changes to take care of myself.

Regards, Danielle

When I emailed Danielle to ask if I might share her email, her response included an updated progress report. As Danielle discovered, mindset is important. Results are often much better when you make your own rules.

Dear Anne,

Thank you for your kind reply. I would be pleased to have you share my experience. I appreciate your attention to privacy; specifically, in this instance, it is because I have also become a practicer of the "mystery" technique. I haven't been telling anybody about the lifestyle changes I've been making, I've simply been making them. That, too, has been a change from times past.

As an update, I've now lost eight pounds. By a rough reckoning, it's taken me a little more than two months to do it and on any diet I'd been on in the past, such "slow" results would have been agonizingly frustrating for me. This time, because I've stayed true to my resolution to concentrate on the process of gradual lifestyle changes and on taking care of myself, it's a wonderful bonus instead.

I've been reading the archived information on the website. In one of the updates, you mentioned a sign that you kept on your desk which said, "You know enough to make your own rules," a thought I found truly inspirational.

Thank you, again, for sharing your experience and techniques through your books and website. Reading your updates to the website a couple of times a week while on coffee break at work is a pleasurable reminder of how to live chic and slim in a culture that reveres a thin physique but promotes a heavy one.

Kind regards, Danielle

᠀ Sometimes you learn as much from mistakes as when you follow the system. The following email describes a first day with *Chic & Slim*.

Dear Ms. Barone,

After returning home from a second European vacation this year and noticing the stark difference between overweight, unhealthy Americans and chic, slender European women, ordering your books was a must. I was delighted to receive all three Chic & Slim books on Friday and promptly devoured the first book that evening. (Note that if I am busy devouring a riveting read, I am not devouring what can be found in my kitchen.)

The very next morning I started putting into practice Le Système Barone. For breakfast, I had a cup of hot English Breakfast tea with a slice of very well made batard bread from a local bakery spread with a small amount of butter and strawberry jam. I didn't think I could possibly be satisfied with just one piece of bread so I sliced two, though spreading just one with butter and jam. I sat down at my table and carefully ate my breakfast. I can't remember the last time I had such a satisfying meal! It tasted divine and sure enough, I was completely satisfied with just the one slice of bread. I put the other slice back.

For lunch I made a hearty stew to accompany the dreary weather. Again, I took a smaller portion than I thought I would be satisfied with and consumed it slowly...and again, I was completely satisfied with it! Like breakfast, I couldn't remember a time when stew was bursting with so much flavor. Mentally and physically, I was very happy simply from tasting the food I was eating.

Then came dinner, when I was derailed from Le Système. A friend came over for dinner and before I knew it, I have wolfed almost my whole meal. I couldn't remember what it tasted like and found myself craving more food because my taste buds weren't satisfied. It struck me like a bolt of lightning how critical it is to a chic and slim lifestyle to slowly chew and savor each forkful of food. Further, I felt terribly bloated and uncomfortable the rest of the evening.

Day One following Le Système Barone was a resounding success and I look forward to incorporating more à la français adjustments into my lifestyle. Thank you from the bottom of my heart for sharing your knowledge!

Best regards, Laura

Note her final comment. She rated Day One a success. Some women might have said, "Oh, I blew it at dinner. This isn't going to work. I will give up." Instead, Laura saw the experience as a lesson in the importance of chewing slowly. Recognizing a habit preventing your weight loss is an element in your future success.

   All women, especially mothers of young children, must make time for themselves. All women need time for relaxation and a time away from our jobs, whether our job is in an office or in our home. Relaxation and restoration is the point of the Boudoir technique in this book. The following two email demonstrate this need. Note the difference in the tone of the first and the second.

Dear Anne,

Thank you so much for all you do. I am a mom who stays home with her three-year-old son and I don't have much time to read but when I need to be cheered up or just to feel in touch with the outside world, I often go to your site. Thank you.

I was reading an article about Mommy Madness—how American mothers are run ragged because of lack of help, competitiveness, etc. I was wondering if you could lead me to information about the

French way of raising children, what advantages they have, etc. I see many mothers at the park who look tired and frankly, downright scruffy (I am sometimes one of them.) Can you help?

Thank you again Anne. All the best, Jacqueline

After I responded with info and a couple of suggestions, a few weeks later, she emailed again.

Dear Anne,

Thank you for answering and also for putting your techniques on the website—they are wonderful!!

I have recently put my son into a preschool for two mornings a week and it is amazing what a little time to oneself can do!! I have actually had lunch with a friend in a French bistro here in Washington twice and it made me feel so good. When I picked up my son I enjoyed him even more because I'd had a break.

Thanks again. All the best, Jacqueline

These emails that I have shared with you demonstrate how any woman can adapt the *Chic & Slim* philosophy to meet her own needs and lifestyle. I hope that as you read the techniques in this book that they spark ideas for ways you can make your unique *Chic & Slim* system simple and quick.

Now on to the techniques: Armoire, Boudoir, Cuisine and Savvy, plus the bonus Blasé.

The first technique is for designing a slim wardrobe, the second for learning the value of an environment for that important relaxation, the third for setting up a slim pantry, the fourth for acquiring a little French savvy. And finally learning to be blasé in the best chic French manner.

I offer these techniques with the hope that soon you will be writing to me with your own *Chic & Slim* success stories. I look forward to hearing from you.

> True elegance is always new
> –it calls for rediscovery and reinvention
> of one's individuality.

Véronique Vienne
French Style

As Véronique Vienne wrote in her wonderful book *French Style*, true elegance demands constant rediscovery and reinvention. For this reason, these techniques are designed to help you in your efforts to rediscover and reinvent your own personal style and unique lifestyle. As you read this book, keep in mind your goals, your hopes and your dreams. Keep in mind that ultra chic and slim version of you.

The Chic & Slim Armoire

Wardrobe Organization for Chic & Slim

Chic French women have small, carefully-planned wardrobes that fit into one small armoire. With only a few pieces, they are always appropriately dressed. They always look marvelously chic. || *American women have huge closets stuffed with clothes. They frequently complain that they have "nothing to wear." They do not always appear appropriately dressed. They do not always look chic.* || ***This technique will help you rid your closets of the excess and design a small, basic wardrobe so you will look attractive and be appropriately dressed for all your lifestyle activities. You may find, as many women have, that getting rid of excess clothes in your closet will help you get rid of excess fat on your body. A slim armoire can help you achieve and keep a slim body.***

SO, YOU WANT TO CREATE a small, something-right-for-every-occasion wardrobe such as the ones that keep those chic French women looking so *fantastique*?

Judging from email I have received, few actions I have suggested for becoming chic and slim *à la française* have given as immediate and satisfying rewards as this first step toward a chic wardrobe I am going to outline for you in the following pages. Again and again in their email and letters, women used the word liberating. Again and again they said getting rid of the excess in their closets jump-started their weight loss.

So while cleaning out your closet may not sound like a terribly exciting starting point (I know, I know, you want to get on to the shopping part),

I think you will find that it will put you on track to weight loss and chic. Even if you already do closet clean-outs on a regular basis, you may find ideas for refining your system and making future closet clean-outs and reorganization speedier and easier. Ready?

Allons-y! Let's go!

THE FIRST NECESSARY STEP

The degree of success and satisfaction you will have in creating that small, chic French-inspired wardrobe depends on this first and very necessary step: you must do something about all those clothes hanging in your closet right now. You must decide which ones you will keep and which ones you will donate to a worthy recipient. The good news here is that, after you do this weeding out of clothes that are wrong for your style, you may find that you have far more that are right than you realized. You will likely find that you need to buy fewer new items than you had thought. Less is almost always more. Often less is enough.

Wardrobe clean-outs and reorganizations work better for me, and create less temporary clutter and mess, if they are done in stages. You may find my first stage in this effort to eliminate the negatives from a closet a bit quirky. But I believe that, if you truly want to be happy and slim, you must get rid of what I call "evil spirit" clothes. Most of us have at least one or two garments that remind us of something unpleasant and depress us when we wear them. They often send us seeking comfort in overeating or plopping down in front of television to watch a movie rather than going out for our exercise.

An evil spirit garment might be a skirt you wore on a date with a guy who turned out to be a total loser. Every time you wear it, you shudder from the vivid mental picture of his nose hairs, his scuffed shoes, and the food stain on his lapel that seemed to be sprouting mold. Or perhaps your evil spirit garment is the faux silk blouse you wore the night that awful woman at the party made all those tacky remarks about your skin. Maybe it is a dress that, every time you wear it, you seem to do something stupid that you later regret. That dress almost seems to jinx you.

Wearing these garments remind you of unpleasant things. Memories of those unpleasant things depress you. But you never think of those unfortunate incidents unless you wear the clothes that you associate with what happened.

Get rid of these evil spirit clothes—if you can possibly afford it. At least rid your closet of the most upsetting. Some of us, however, have unpleasant things happen to us on such a regular basis that, if we give away all the clothes that remind us of those incidents, we might have to become part-time nudists. Use your judgment.

Once you have completed this first stage and cleaned out the evil spirit clothes, the next stage is to rid your closet of anything that does not fit, is not your personal style, or does not make you look wonderful.

Many women keep in their closets clothing that is several sizes smaller than they have worn in the last decade. Unless you think your granddaughters are going to be into wearing Retro, it might be best to let these items go on to resale with the idea that, should you again achieve a size 4 or whatever, you could reward yourself with a new wardrobe. On the other hand, you should not assume the fit of clothes you have not worn in many months. Don't guess. Check. Put them on your body and stand in front of a full length mirror and make a valid assessment of whether or not these items fit properly. While you are at it, evaluate whether they are your personal style and whether or not they make you look attractive.

For garments that do not fit properly but flatter, you have to make a judgment as to whether they can be altered. If they can, then, you must be realistic about whether or not you will actually have the time to do the adjustments yourself, or the willingness to spend what is necessary to pay someone to make the alterations for you.

Certainly a classic $400 suit is a more likely a candidate for alteration than a $23.99 trendy skirt. Changing the hem in skirt or pants is something most of us can accomplish, especially if we use that very convenient iron-on tape. To use the iron-on tape to adjust a hem, you do not even have to know how to thread a needle, though you do have to own an iron.

Taking the waistband off pants or a skirt that fits in the hips but is too large in the waist, resizing the darts and reattaching the waistband requires more skill. Do not tackle this job unless you are reasonably sure of your ability. As for your angora sweater your maid shrunk in the dryer on high heat, you might as well resign yourself to giving it to some small, needy child. I have never had great success resizing wool once it has been damaged by high temperatures. Nor, for that matter, reshaping wool that has been stretched, though some people claim it can be done.

Experience has shown me that actually trying on clothes during the clean-out process is worth the time. Sometimes I find that a piece of clothing may have more possibilities than I remember. For example, several years ago I had to have emergency surgery. A short time before that surgery, I had bought a dress from which I had not yet even removed the tags by the time I went to the hospital. Somehow, in the confusion of the surgery and recuperation, that dress was pushed to the back of the closet and forgotten.

After the surgery, when I was sufficiently recovered that I could do one of my periodic closet clean-outs, I found the dress. I decided that I had made a mistake in buying it, more lured by the 75 percent off original price than how it actually looked on my body. I decided I would give it away. I hung the dress in the foyer closet with other items I planned to donate. But before I actually took this dress to Goodwill, an unexpected event came up that required I wear a dress.

One thing you must accept if you maintain a small wardrobe as those chic French women do: you must keep up with laundry and dry cleaning. Otherwise, you may truly find yourself with "nothing to wear." At least, nothing clean. (Though my late sister-in-law insisted that in an emergency, you could dig something out of the laundry hamper, spray it with scented spray starch, and put it in the dryer on air setting for 10 minutes, take it out and wear it. I have never tried this.)

But back to my story about the dress. I was behind in laundry. With nothing else appropriate, I grabbed the dress out of the closet, pulled off the tags and put it on. *Quelle surprise!* That dress looked great on me. Because of my healing incision, my doctor had not yet allowed me to resume my regular exercise program. That dress hid some areas that were not as toned as usual. That dress became my wear-anywhere-for-anything dress until I was able to resume exercise and get myself back in shape.

So before you part with an item you have not worn in several months, try it on. Your body may have changed shape, or you may have forgotten exactly how great you looked wearing it. Fashion may have changed. I have been amused at the number of times that I have bought something that was not truly stylish at the time I bought it. I made the purchase simply because I liked the item and it looked good on me. Then, about the time it was showing wear, its style became very much "in."

Over the years I have learned two important lessons about wardrobe maintenance. The first lesson: Do not be hasty discarding clothes. The second lesson: When you think you have nothing to wear, shop your closet. You may find clothing you have forgotten, or which now fits your lifestyle better than previously. Even when you keep a small wardrobe as I do, you may discover items you have forgotten, or at least forgotten all their possibilities.

When you have removed from your closet all the evil spirit clothes, all those that do not fit, all those that do not show you at your best, all those that are worn out or beyond mending, all those you do not like, and all those that are not appropriate for your unique personal style, what next?

SORTING, MENDING, ALTERING

If you have sorted out clothes for mending and alteration, put them in a cardboard box or shopping bag clearly labeled Mend & Alter, and put the box or bag where you see it daily. If you have not done anything about mending or alteration in two weeks, face the fact that you probably will not find the time, and reconsider your decision about these items.

A word on how you sort these culled items: Some like to sort into large plastic bags. Plastic bags won't hold their mouths open. But if you have a box for each category sitting open, you can toss items into the correct box. Sorting goes faster.

Another reason I prefer boxes for sorting is because you can more easily label them for their destinations such as the church clothes closet, Salvation Army Thrift Store, resale, or the person to whom you are giving the clothes. If you do use large plastic bags, you may have to apply masking tape and write on the tape. Though lighter colored bags can be more easily labeled with a marker pen than black bags. But do label. Labeling saves confusion. One woman I know sorted into black plastic bags with no labels. Then, later, she mistakenly tossed into the dumpster the bag of items needing mending. It took time and the assistance of an agile neighborhood child who could climb into the apartment building's dumpster and retrieve the bag.

A WORD ABOUT REGRETS

Once you rid your closet of all the wrong items that are not going to be part of your new wardrobe, you are ready to organize a chic wardrobe *à la française*. But before we progress to closet organization, let me say something about Regrets. Almost always eliminating excess brings positive feelings. But, invariably, after a rigorous clean-out, there will come some moment weeks or months later when you will regret having discarded one or two particular items. When this moment comes, I want you to remember the personal experience I am going to relate to you.

Several years ago I discovered in a discount store and bought a lightweight periwinkle pink cotton jacket. With its three-quarter sleeves it seemed perfect for cool mornings and to camouflage certain age arms. But after the first washing I discovered that it required ironing, was a pain to iron and somehow, after that first washing, looked a little too low-quality for my personal style. My mother was collecting items for the church clothes closet for the needy, so I gave the jacket to my mother for that cause.

The next summer, the problems with the jacket had faded from my memory. I remembered only the positive points about the jacket that caused me to buy it in the first place. I regretted that I had given it away. Then, I discovered that my mother (for whatever reason) had not taken the jacket to the church clothes closet. There it was, hanging in the closet in her guest room. Elated, I carried the jacket home. Very quickly I again discovered that it was hard to iron and looked tacky even when ironed. For the second time it went out the door. This time for good.

When you have regrets about some item you have given away, remember my pink jacket. And remember that discarded clothes are often like ex-boyfriends: in later memory they may seem more wonderful than they really were.

ORGANIZING YOUR CLOSET FOR CHIC

Now, on to organizing your newly liberated closet. A workable organization system for your closet will make it possible for you to see what is available and to allow you to make the right choice quickly. Think how many minutes of your life you have spent standing in front of the closet trying to decide what you are going to wear. Then, trying to find the garment you decided on.

If you do not have a system, you need to devise one. Or, if your old system was based on a different sort of wardrobe, you may need to modify the system for a small, chic wardrobe of the French sort. If you have first rid your closet of excess, organizing will be much easier than it would have been without the clean-out. Also, you will probably have more energy and enthusiasm for creating your new wardrobe when you have done the prior paring down. You have banished frumpy clothes from your closets. You are ready for chic.

What kind of closet organization system do you need? Through the decades I have read numerous magazine articles and books that outline a particular author's successful system. Moving around the world as I have and living in an assortment of housing and climates, I have found that successful closet organization depends on the type and number of closets you have as well as how many seasons your wardrobe must service. Good closet organization also must take into consideration your lifestyle requirements. If you are currently living in a three bedroom ranch style house in a small rural community and working at home and caring for small children, and if most of your socializing is backyard cookouts with relatives and friends, you will need one sort of closet organization (and wardrobe). You will likely not find appropriate the same organization system useful to a corporate executive who lives in an apartment in New York City, who travels worldwide on a regular basis, who is an avid weekend gardener and hiker when at her country home, and who must attend many formal events with her husband.

When I was a Peace Corps Volunteer in equatorial Africa, there was only one season: hot. Armoire organization is very simple when your entire wardrobe consists of four cotton shift dresses and an extra pair of sandals. Now that I live where recent winters the weather has been schizophrenic (one week's high is 81 degrees F, the next week's high is 21 degrees F), and, even during the sultry summer months, the fierce air-conditioning in some stores and homes means that in one afternoon I might need clothing comfortable for temperatures from 116 degrees outdoors to 68 degrees indoors. Because of weather extremes, most of the year I need clothes for at least two seasons.

Some closets give easy access to the whole rod. In others, accessibility to all clothes you wear frequently is a challenge. In the 1920s-era apartment where I was living when I wrote the first version of *Chic & Slim Techniques*, my bedroom closet measured 41 inches wide. Not much space there. When I initially drafted this chapter, during winter, I took an inventory of that 41-inch closet. On the far right hung my two full length coats and my winter lounging robe. To their left, two jackets, one skirt, one dress, finally my one pant suit. To the left of the pant suit hung my four pair of jeans. Two pair were new, purchased at recent sales, one pair had been in service six months, and the other, an ancient pair, was suitable for grungy jobs such as major housecleaning and gardening.

In the center of my closet hung my shirts (3), sweaters (5), and turtlenecks (3). My exercise pants and top hung at the far left of the closet. One wool sweater that could not be hung was folded and boxed on a shelf above the rod. Shoes in boxes, and scarves and berets in a clear plastic zippered bag sat on a higher shelf. When the weather turned cool, all I had retained from my summer wardrobe was one dress, a couple of cotton knit tops, one pair cotton pants, and one pair lightweight jeans. These items were folded and bagged on the closet's upper shelf.

A small closet necessitated a small wardrobe. Fortunately, at that time, my lifestyle did not require formal evening clothes nor a lot of clothing for cold weather wear. I would have had difficulty finding room for them. Yet, for the clothes that were necessary for my lifestyle at that time, my system made the best of the limited space.

THE BEST ARRANGEMENT

What is the best way to arrange clothes and accessories? Every woman of chic style I have known over the years has maintained an organized closet. Organization may not be an absolute necessity for chic. But it is certainly an aid.

The system that works for me is to group clothes by categories. This works for me because, at any time, the total number of items in any one category is small. In the section for tops, I have (left to right) sleeveless, short-sleeved, three-quarter, and finally long-sleeved. Even if I have only one of each, it is easier to find what I want quickly when I know that the further to the left, the shorter the sleeve. If I had more clothes, I might choose to put all the shirts in one section, all the sweaters in another, all the T-shirts in another. From time to time, I experiment with different arrangements, always keeping in mind that the goal is finding the item I want easily and quickly.

Some women prefer to arrange their closets by color group. Think in terms of the color spectrum. Beginning on the left you hang: white, pink, red, orange/gold, yellow, green, light blue, navy blue, deep purple, lavender, beige, brown, black. Other women find it useful to hang outfits together. So your black wool suit and your ivory silk blouse you always wear with it would make one grouping. Your jade jeans, green/black knit top, and black pullover would make another. To further refine this system, you hang the most dressy outfits on one side and work toward the most casual on the other. You can also include belts, special lingerie, tights, or socks in these groupings. Belts can be slipped over hanger necks, socks tucked into jeans pockets. This system might be particularly useful for someone who has difficulty waking up in the morning and who tends to dash out the door in mismatched outfits.

The important thing is to arrange your clothes in a system that works well for you and your current lifestyle. (I know that I keep repeating some version of this modify-to-work-best-for-you instruction, but it really is a key factor in your success.) Your goal is to make it easy to see what you have available and to avoid wasting precious time hunting. You want to prevent spending ten minutes pawing through the hangers muttering, "I know I have an oxford cloth shirt in here somewhere."

POST A SYSTEM GUIDE

Once you devise your system, it will help to make a system guide and tack it up in view in your closet. This can be as simple as a handwritten list on an index card, or it can be as elaborate as a beautifully designed computer printout in ornate fonts printed on card stock. Your aim is a visual that makes it easy to replace items according to your system, not just stick them in the closet helter-skelter promising yourself that you will rearrange the clothes in the correct system tomorrow, or next week, or when you have time. I know, I know, sometimes when we are exhausted, we just don't bother with a system. Sometimes when we are exhausted we leave clothes in a heap on the floor. But in the long run it pays to keep the closet as orderly as possible. You gain the satisfaction of feeling in control. You will surely achieve chic more consistently.

Designing your closet system, think practical use. If your organization is too complicated to follow on a regular basis, it is useless. For the easiest, most basic system, you can group your clothing on hangers in four groups: tops, skirts, pants, and anything else street or full length. Short jackets can hang with tops. Longer garments should, of course, hang where they can hang down without touching something sitting on the floor below that might wrinkle them, or worse snag and tear them.

If your closet has shelves, once you have the hanging garments organized, you can arrange the shoes, handbags, and other items that sit on shelves or hang from hooks. You apply the same culling and sorting system described above for clothing for your accessories.

Once this organization is accomplished, you can move on to what you have in dresser drawers. This might include lingerie, tights, nylon stockings, socks, gloves, and scarves, as well as sleepwear. Again, always do the arrangement that pleases and helps you. On the other hand, experimenting on a small scale with a new systems is sometimes a path to devising an improved system.

SECTION BY SECTION WORKS BEST

Clean out and organize section by section. You will complete the job more quickly, see order restored to your living space, and feel a sense of satisfaction for a goal accomplished. You will be less likely to have a crisis interrupt and force you to abandon the task mid-mess.

I truly wish that I had photographs of some chic French women's closets I have seen. The neatness and precision of arrangement are almost impossible to describe in words. A particular image, however, comes to mind as I write this. Once I was in the room when a French friend opened a drawer in a chest of drawers to look for something. She had a small apartment and many treasures accumulated in a life that had been quite affluent. Every inch of space in that drawer had been utilized, and the arrangement of items a geometric work of art. Utilitarian sculpture is one way I might describe it.

Hard as I have tried, I have never achieved the degree of order and neatness and use of space that I have observed in the homes of French women. But my efforts to emulate that observed order and neatness has paid dividends in making my life better and my body slimmer.

ORGANIZING A CHIC AND SLIM WARDROBE

Now that all the wrong clothes have been eliminated from your life, you are ready to organize a chic wardrobe *a la française*.

Like a chic French woman, your *Chic & Slim* goals are that everything in your wardrobe works for your personal style, and that the clothes you wear make you feel good about yourself. You want to feel *bien dans sa peau*, well in your skin, as the French say. You also need clothing appropriate for your age and lifestyle. Inherent in this appropriateness is the requirement that your clothing purchases are within your budget. French women manage marvelous chic on relatively small amounts of money. Yet American women have long had more sources for buying quality at bargain prices than their European sisters, so there is absolutely no reason anyone in the USA should go into debt to dress well.

During my most impecunious era, when I was writing the original *Chic & Slim*, the additions to my wardrobe that became its most important pieces were a new, still-with-tags black knit Banana Republic dress ($7), an almost new pair of black Arizona jeans ($2), a very chic Calvin Klein tan skirt ($5) and a cashmere wool sweater in a favorite shade of amethyst ($5). All happy finds at the my local Hospice Thrift Shop. When absolutely necessary, you can dress well on very little money.

In previous *Chic & Slim* books and in website discussions, I have discussed extensively personal style. For the purposes of this technique, I will assume that you are familiar with the *Chic & Slim* style philosophy and have been developing a chic look that is unique to you. If you are not familiar with that concept and process, you can read the original *Chic & Slim*.

THE BASIC CHIC FRENCH WARDROBE

First we will look at what makes a chic French woman's basic wardrobe. Next we will explore how we can use the French chic wardrobe as the blueprint for building a small, stylish wardrobe that makes us look attractive and appropriately dressed for any situation in which we are likely to find ourselves, no matter where in the world we live.

At its most minimalist, a chic French wardrobe is a skirt, a sweater, and a good scarf. (In some age groups it might be a pair of jeans, a sweater, and a good scarf.) In any case, three pieces. That's it.

In those difficult days following the end of World War II, a skirt, a sweater, and a scarf constituted the wardrobe of any number of women, not just in France, but across Europe and Great Britain. In the biographies of actresses Sophia Loren and Audrey Hepburn there are accounts of how, at that time, each of these women managed to look chic with just such a limited wardrobe. Sophia Loren in Rome recounted she dyed both her skirt and blouse black to make her ensemble more chic. A friend of Audrey Hepburn in London explained how the young woman, who in a few years would become the French designer Givenchy's muse, accessorized her basic skirt and sweater with scarves and a little hat that she folded in different ways to give variety to her look.

In the original *Chic & Slim* I quote the French-born writer Véronique Vienne who describes her wardrobe in 1965 as one dress, two skirts, four turtlenecks, one pearl necklace, one black patent-leather belt, two pairs of Charles Jourdan shoes, two silk scarves, an antique Piaget watch, and a Mont Blanc pen.

In an article by Sheila Johnston in *The Independent*'s Online Edition she describes actress Charlotte Rampling at a recent interview in Paris. "Rampling is looking good — very good . . . . She wears black cigarette pants and a crisp white shirt: classic French chic quickened with the shock multicoloured splash of a tailored floral jacket."

This, by the way, is a great example of the chic French habit of combining classics (black pants and white shirt) with something trendy.

FRENCH FASHION TRENDS

Fashion continually evolves. Two changes recently observed in France are that French women are buying more bargain chic, and that personal styles are becoming more casual. Despite French women's reputation for living their lives in high heels, recent visitors to Paris report seeing more flats and mid-heel shoes on female French feet.

Traditionally, French women bought high quality classics whose prices reflected that quality. Until a few years ago, French women really had little choice. While they were clever at having a seamstress copy couture fashions or sewing these copies themselves, at finding samples sales, and stretching their wardrobes with flea market finds and clothing inherited from an aunt or mother, French women did not have available the wide range of qualities and prices that have been common in the USA for decades. But various entrepreneurs and multinational corporations have now made bargain chic available in France. French women, who have always been very responsive to fashion trends, have begun to incorporate trendy, less expensive items into their wardrobes.

Other factors are at work here. In fashion, the distinction between high end and low end is blurring. Pulitzer Prize-winning fashion writer Robin Givhan explained in a *Washington Post* article "Thread & Circus: Sell Clothes Based on Their Merits? Bo-ring! Fashion Tries Making a Spectacle of Its Sell."

She wrote: "It used to be that fashion brands were distinguished by quality and creativity. Buying a fancy designer label meant purchasing a well-made garment and one whose creator had been touched by a muse. They were clothes that could not be found—at least not readily—at lower prices." But today, with a few notable exceptions, designers are selling mood and attitude, not quality in design and craftsmanship. Theatrical shows of a designer's new collection and celebrity endorsements (when sometimes the designer is the celebrity), not quality and unique design, sell the clothes.

There was a day in the past when quality or lack of it in a garment was obvious. Robin Givhan writes: "An expensive suit once looked like it was worth the money that had been paid for it and a cheap suit obviously reflected its modest price. Now, those with even a modest income have access to good tailoring. Cashmere was once a luxury reserved only for those willing to pay a premium. Now it is a staple of the mass market. The most current styles once came at a high cost, and bargain hunters had to wait for the newest silhouettes to trickle down. Now, the trendiest ideas are quickly available at throwaway prices at H&M and Zara."

Good design is becoming increasingly available in budget priced clothes. In 2004, Karl Lagerfeld, who had long designed for Chanel, created a lower-priced line for the Swedish mass marketer H&M. An article on *style.com* quoted J. Mendel designer Gilles Mendel. "To popularize that sense of couture, to make high design available at a low price point, is very much the mentality of European people. That someone like Karl is doing this just brings a bigger audience to high fashion, and that's a great thing."

Karl Lagerfeld explained his willingness to design the line. "My concept of ready-to-wear today at whatever level is that it has to be as good as the most expensive brand. Design is very important, and design is not a question of price anymore." And that is very good news for the millions of moderate incomes who want to wear good design.

NOW WE ALL CAN KNOW THE SECRETS
Another democratic change for the fashion conscious is that shoppers all over the world today are better informed about merchandise available. Information that was once the well-kept secrets of the fashion industry is now available to shoppers to help them get the most for their money. Books such as shopping authority Suzy Gershman's *Best Dressed* explain how clothes are manufactured and retailed. With this inside information, anyone can shop the right places at the right times for the best prices on clothing and accessories. They can avoid being a victim of retailers' marketing strategies and dress well without spending a fortune.

The Internet, through such means as blogs and consumer buyer review forums, also help savvy shoppers learn how and where to get value for their money. Online shopping and mail-order catalogs give a fashion conscious woman an astounding number of sources from which to build her wardrobe far beyond merchandise in her local shops and mall. A warning here. The Internet is also the place where a lot of cheap designer knockoffs are sold. Images on a computer screen can be deceptive. To protect yourself from buying cheap copies rather than the name brand, you must buy from a reputable source. I would suspect that if you are going to invest in a Hermès scarf, you would be wise to buy it from Hermès or one of the name department stores that sell the brand, rather than an eBay auction. On the other hand, if you are going to buy a copy, make sure that the price and the quality are in balance. A lot of fashion savvy women buy copies at copy prices. Sometimes it is impossible for representatives of the name brand companies to tell the difference between the real and the knockoff. The key here is to know what you are getting and pay accordingly. If possible, inspect the original. Then when you see a copy, you will be able to judge how close the copy comes to the original in materials and craftsmanship.

This discussion of originals vs. copies brings to mind a neighbor in the 1950s. She was an elegant woman who achieved her elegance on her husband's moderate income. She was a talented seamstress and sewed many of her dresses. Once, years before she had owned a Neiman Marcus dress. When that dress went out of style, she carefully removed the label from the dress and sewed it into one she had made herself. When that dress went out of style, she again transferred the label to a new dress she had sewed. She said wearing a dress, even a homemade one, with the Neiman Marcus label made her feel more elegant. And of course, French women have long been feeling and looking elegant by whipping up their own copies of designer fashions, with or without a transferred label.

I do not know if the classes are still offered. But a woman I knew who lived in Paris in the 1960s took a tailoring class there to learn the sewing techniques used in the French couture houses. With the skills she learned, she created herself a premium champagne wardrobe on a *vin de table* budget. One lesson she learned in the classes that she shared with me was always put in a zipper by hand, not on a machine. The improvement in the way the garment looks on your body is worth the extra effort. That certainly proved true in my own sewing.

A BASIC CHIC WARDROBE FOR THE REST OF US

What is required for a French-inspired *Chic & Slim* wardrobe for these early years of the 21st century?

My *Chic & Slim* Essentials give you room to make your own personal style choices as to specific colors and styles within the parameters of the category. Additionally, a number of you have requested information on how to dress during the time you are Chic-On-The-Way-To-Slim. My *Chic & Slim* wardrobe essentials list takes into account that most chic French women are slim, or, if overweight, only what the rest of the world would consider plump. Some of the items French women deem essential to their wardrobes may not be the best for a larger-size woman until she progresses further down the road toward slim. I have attempted to make each essentials category sufficiently comprehensive that you make the choice within that category that works best for the size and lifestyle that you have now. I repeat now.

YOUR *C'EST MOI* AND *C'EST MOI AUSSI* COLORS

French women build their basic wardrobe around a neutral color that works well with their skin tones and hair. If you have not already, you also should decide on a basic neutral color around which you build your wardrobe. By my late twenties, I had more or less decided that brown was the best choice for a neutral color around which to build my wardrobe. I think of it as my *C'est Moi* (That's Me) color. It took a few more years of trial and error before I settled on a *C'est Moi Aussi* (That's Me Too) color, a secondary basic neutral personal style color that works well with your primary neutral choice. For me, that was a rich plum color. Various hues of both colors from cream to sienna in the brown, and from pale lavender to a dark raisin in the purple all work well together and with my skin and hair coloring.

True, in the years after *Chic & Slim* was published, black and red dominated my wardrobe to coordinate with the *Chic & Slim* book covers and to dress in colors more likely to be worn by French women. (Ah, the rigorous demands of marketing!) But one morning I opened my closet doors, looked in, and decided I really no longer wanted all that red and black, even though the colors work well for me. So while I have kept the good red and black pieces, most all my new purchases made subsequently have been in *C'est Moi* browns and *C'est Moi Aussi* plums and related berry pinks.

This does not mean that forever I will only wear only browns and plums. Personal style evolves. You adapt it over the years to your needs and lifestyle at any particular time.

If you have not yet settled on a neutral color for the basis of your wardrobe, what are the best candidates? Black is a basic wardrobe neutral color French women are likely to choose. It is a good choice for the USA, as well. Almost any year you can surely find a black skirt or basic black dress of decent quality at a fair price available in any city. You might not find the selection as good for other neutrals. Some years you just cannot find much in brown or gray. Green and burgundy can be even more elusive.

Black is said to mix with anything. Brown does not hide most stains as well as black, a color that allows even the food-spill prone of us to look chic. But brown mixes more harmoniously with many colors. For the aesthetic taste of many of us, brown will work more acceptably than black with shades of pink and orange, for example. If you are clever, you can make brown work with navy, especially if you accent with some tangerine or perhaps a paisley blouse or scarf that includes both brown and navy in the paisley design. Navy and gray are also good choices for that dark neutral color. With brown, navy, or gray, a dark shade that approaches black is the most workable. I also like loden green or burgundy for a basic wardrobe neutral. A classic red or deep persimmon does not have the slimming facility of burgundy or dark burnt orange, but they are often more harmonious with darker skin than other choices. Here is a place where you may have to make a choice on which is more important, looking slim or wearing a flattering color that makes you look a tad plumper, but overall more attractive.

HOW DO YOU KNOW THE COLOR IS RIGHT?

How do you know when you have picked the basic neutral wardrobe colors that are absolutely right for you? In the film version of *A Chorus Line*, the Zach character tells the Cassie character that "there should be a law against you wearing that color." Her audition dance leotard is a rich burgundy that is absolutely perfect for actress Alyson Reed's skin and hair color.

Perhaps no man will tell you that you look so seductive and irresistible wearing a particular color that there should be a law against your doing so. But reactions from others who see you will be an excellent indication of what colors work best for you. You can also get help by looking at others who have basically your skin and hair color and see what looks good on them. Park yourself in a place where well dressed women will be walking past and do an hour or so of analysis.

So what essential items do you need in your closet so that you can be well-dressed for almost all occasions? Those of you familiar with previous *Chic & Slim* books and articles may be puzzled that I have left out three categories important in a chic French woman's wardrobe: shoes, lingerie and fragrance. But I have purposely narrowed the focus for this basic wardrobe.

Chic & Slim WARDROBE ESSENTIALS
- Skirt or Dress
- Sweater
- Pants
- Suit
- Dressy Blouse or Top
- Jeans or Other Casual Pants
- Casual shirt
- Knit Tops
- Scarf
- Hat

SKIRT OR DRESS

Skirt or dress? Skirts worn with blouses require either a shirttail tucked in, or the proper length to look flattering on the outside. (Tricky if you are taller or shorter than average.) For perfectly slim women a shirttail tucked in is generally not a problem. But for women who are Chic-On-The-Way-To-Slim, a skirt and blouse, if they are of different colors, even different textures, can sometimes accent plumpness. A dress in a solid dark color without a defined waistline, on the other hand, has strong slimming potential. I have a Ralph Lauren black knit dress without a defined waist that I can wear either without belt, or pulled up a couple of inches and draped over with a black belt for a blouson effect. Either way, this dress is the most slimming garment I own. No skirt and top, or pants and top outfit comes close to equaling it.

For a woman not yet as slim as she plans to be, a perfectly fitting dress in a dark neutral shade in a good knit or soft wool might be a good choice as the foundation on which their everyday cool weather wardrobe is built. For the pseudo-slim, that is, a woman who weighs a bit more than the weight at which she looks her best, a dress of this sort might make her appear to have instantly shed 20 pounds.

French women often choose such a basic dress in the sleeveless version. They wear it in warmer months as a dress. As the weather becomes cooler, they wear it over a short-sleeved or three-quarter sleeved top — or long-sleeved light-weight blouse. Then, in the winter, they add a pullover or cardigan sweater buttoned up. With a sweater worn over the dress, the dress appears to be a skirt. This way, the sleeveless dress can be worn year round. Worn with different sweaters and shirts, as well as with different scarves and jewelry, gives the illusion of having a more extensive wardrobe than one actually has.

SWEATER

I have never found cardigans as useful in my wardrobe as French women do. Their cardigan sweaters are often beautiful hand-knitted ones that can do duty as a jacket, especially for women whose clothing budgets might not stretch to a wool jacket. (This was truer in the decades before bargain chic became more available and when a wool jacket was a major investment.) I always noticed that most French women's magazines included knitting patterns for sweaters. At least in years past, many French women knitted their own sweaters providing themselves with the exact color and fit their personal style required.

My own sweater preference is for turtlenecks. They fit my personal style and they are a good choice for my neck. But the sweater must be a true turtleneck. I need the width that comes from the fold over or bunching you can do with a true turtleneck. Mock turtlenecks require a camouflaging scarf.

Whether your preference is for a cardigan, crew or V-neck pullover, turtleneck, or polo style, at least one sweater is necessary for a chic wardrobe. Even if you live in the tropics, you need a sweater in your wardrobe for that odd day it is cool, or when you make a trip to more temperate climates.

The chief requirement for color for your essential sweater is that it works with all pieces of your *Chic & Slim* Essentials suit. For a French woman, the sweater preference has long been cashmere. Lately, cashmere, once was an expensive luxury, is now available at more moderate prices.

In addition to cashmere, there are other beautiful wools. I have always been fond of angora (from rabbit) and merino (from Italy.) For those allergic to wool, or for those who do not care to be bothered with the extra care wool usually requires, there are many synthetics or synthetic and natural fiber blends in which beautiful sweaters are made. You have many choices from which to choose the absolutely perfect one.

PANTS

Pants are so much a part of almost every well dressed woman's wardrobe that it is hard to imagine that only a few decades ago pants were only acceptable attire for women in the most casual of circumstances. At my university in the early 1960s, women were forbidden wearing even dressy wool slacks to class during the most frigid of snowstorms. Should we be so brazen to do so, we could be expelled.

When pant suits came along a few years later, at first, many restaurants (and other establishments) barred entrance to women who wore them. That was until a number of women, when challenged, reached for their zippers and took off the offending pants right there in front of God, the maitre d' and startled diners.

When it comes to finding that perfect pair of pants to meet this essential requirement in your *Chic & Slim* wardrobe, you must accept two facts. The first is that finding the pants that are the right fit and are the right length may mean that you have to try on fifty, perhaps more than fifty, pairs to find ones in the fabric and color you want. The second fact you must accept is that pants are less forgiving than dresses or skirts when you gain or lose a few pounds. Lose five pounds and the pants that fit perfectly lose their chic to bagginess. Gain five pounds and they pull in the crotch and across the tummy, diminishing chic.

Pants that look marvelous worn with high stiletto heels will usually be too long to look as chic with flats or even a loafer with a one inch heel. Decide what shoes you will wear with your pants and have those shoes on your feet when you try on the pants. Don't guess. Make certain the length is right, unless you know the hems can be adjusted. Lined pants, of course, require more effort to adjust the hem than unlined. Whenever shopping, it is always a good idea to try on garments wearing the exact lingerie and shoes that you intend to wear with that garment. This is even more important with pants.

The first shipment of winter pants arrive in the stores near the end of July. You might be out shopping in your very flat sandals. The pants may be just the right length with the sandals. But in October when the weather turns cool, and you put on those new wool slacks with your new high-heeled boots, you may discover that those pants are too short. Likewise, the pants that looked right in the seat when you were wearing cotton underpants may look different when you put them on with control top pantyhose or some of those industrial strength slimming garments a previous generation called girdles but which have been renamed shapewear. Doesn't shapewear sound much more chic?

French women are very particular about the length of both skirts and pants. Some are so inclined to exactness in these measurements that they choose to wear a pair of pants with only one heel height. French women are known for adjusting the length of pants or a skirt a mere one-fourth inch to get the length that they consider exactly right. They are willing to pay for alterations to get that length that they consider the most flattering.

As for the color for these essential pants, they should be in a basic neutral shade, but perhaps not the same as your essential suit. In any case, the color needs to be one that will work with the same shirts, blouses, and sweaters that you wear with your suit. So if black is the basic color for your suit, you might want a gray or pin stripe for your essential pants. If your basic neutral color for your suit is navy, you might choose burgundy or a classic red for your essential pants.

Another possibility is to use the same neutral color for your pants as the suit, but choose pants in a tweed or tiny herringbone check. Both of these last two choices would mean your tops should be solid color if your personal style tends more toward the classic than the avant-garde.

As for fabric choice for pants, any number of synthetics are easy care and can be worn all year, especially in locations where indoors is often fiercely air-conditioned in summer. All-season wools are also a possibility if your budget can stand the additional cost for dry cleaning.

SUIT

A suit is chic. A suit is serious fashion. Depending on your lifestyle and your personal style, your *Chic & Slim* essential suit might be the most important outfit in your closet. Or it might be totally unnecessary.

As a writer who works in a home office and lives in an area where casual dressing is the norm, I do not often need a suit. But occasions do arise when I am glad that I have one.

Your essential suit would likely be in your *C'est Moi* color that you have designated your personal style color. Everything else in your *Chic & Slim* essentials wardrobe should work with the suit to extend the possibilities for variety in your wardrobe.

Two or three piece suit, which do you need? Most fashion authorities today suggest that for the lives of most women in the USA, a suit comprised of jacket, skirt, and pants as the most practical. But what if you rarely wear a skirt? Is a suit comprised of just jacket and pants okay? Of course. And if you always wear skirts, never pants, then it is pointless to have a pair hanging in your closet.

I offer a suggestion here for the Chic-On-The-Way-To-Slim. If neither skirts or pants are flattering to your figure, then think in terms of a jacket and dress for your suit. With the right design and color, a large woman will surely look slimmer and more elegant in a dress and jacket of the same fabric than in a more conventional jacket and pants or skirt suit.

What about the fabric from which the suit is made? Must all the suit's pieces be made of the same fabric? Absolutely not. In fact, if you have been shopping for suits lately, you see that often the jacket will be of one fabric and the pants and skirt of another. These days many suits are offered with each piece sold separately. This practice is much welcomed by women who are one size above the waist and another size below, as well as for those who might like to build their own suits. One part of the designer's creation might not suit a personal style or body build.

Like French women, I like combining different textures and slightly different shades of the same color for one outfit. The jacket of the suit that I fell in love with when I saw the runway photos just wasn't right for me. Though I did eventually buy it when I found it later 75% off in my size. But it really does not look right on my body. Maybe if I grew another six or eight inches (or bought stilts), I would look as chic as that model whose photo made the suit so appealing. At my height, I look as if I have borrowed some man's jacket. Despite my problems with the mid-thigh jacket, when I tried on the pants, they fit and looked so right and felt so comfortable that I bought them and then set out to find another jacket to wear with them.

Once I found a jacket, then I began the hunt for a skirt that would work with the jacket. The one I eventually bought is actually a more cocoa shade of brown than the pants. But that hardly matters since I will never wear the skirt and pants at the same time, will I? Both work well with the tweed jacket that I found.

I do not wear the suit often, but I am prepared with something that is absolutely right for me whenever a situation arises that demands it. I avoid a last-minute frantic shopping trip on which I might have to pay too much for something that did not really fit my personal style.

DRESSY BLOUSE OR TOP

A dressy blouse or other top can work magic. You are wearing jeans and a knit tank top. Off comes the tank and on goes the top. Add some earrings or a pretty necklace. Especially if you trade your flat shoes for some strappy heels or a pair of high-heeled boots, suddenly you have elegance.

A dressy blouse or top is important to a *Chic & Slim* Essentials wardrobe, not just for dramatic change it can make to take you from casual to elegant without changing the pants or skirt you are wearing. A dressy blouse or top is necessary to pair with your essential suit to take it to its maximum elegance for times that demand more formality. You note that I have said a silky blouse or top rather than a silk blouse or top. There are so many wonderful synthetics now that look as lovely as silk and that have the advantages of easy care and more economical price than real silk that real silk is not necessary for elegance.

Though I must admit that, like French women, I love real silk. During the years I lived in India I had an opportunity to learn about silks. I spent countless hours in shops whose shelves were lined with hundreds of bolts of silks in a multitude of colors, weights, patterns, qualities, and textures. I even toured silk factories and held little silk worms in my hand and watched them spin the little cocoons.

While I lived in India, I bought much silk and oversaw the tailoring of many beautiful silk garments for myself and for my family. The luxurious feel of real silk against my skin gives me a satisfaction that the synthetics do not.

Silk, like cashmere wool, is a beautiful and sensual fabric.

The variety of silks is large. One piece I enjoy as a throw is a length of Indian wild silk. My tailor was clever at cutting. After I had a dress made from the length of fabric I had a generous amount left. Wild silk should not be confused with raw silk. Raw silk is also rough-textured but made from cocoons of domestic silk worms that are farmed, like goats or sheep are farmed. The difference in silk farming is that the livestock are wiggly little worms on big rattan trays, not four-footed animals in pastures.

Wild silk is made from cocoons of wild silk worms that spin their cocoons in trees in the forest. They are collected by hunters who go out and gather them from the branches. Wild silk is a rough, heavy silk. My piece is unbleached and undyed, still with its natural colors. These silk fibers make a variegated cloth of shades ranging from a creamy ivory to dark mahogany. The original cloth made a very elegant A-line dress with plain round neck and cap sleeves that I wore to women's teas and to receptions that required a nice dress and heels.

Today much lovely silk clothing is available for sale in the USA and at reasonable prices. If you have never worn silk, you should at least try on some good pieces to enjoy the feel against your skin. Silk sweaters are not only elegant, but they are very warm for their light weight. A silk turtleneck fits under a jacket without bulk. Silk long underwear feels lovely against the skin and keeps you warm without marring the fit of the body-hugging styles. So while you might have your necessary elegance from faux silks, you might consider one blouse or sweater of real silk. Watch for sales and clearances if your budget is tight.

A blouse is elegant and traditional, but if you are the more modern type, then certainly an elegant sweater might perform the essential role of an essential dressy top.

JEANS OR OTHER CASUAL PANTS

Forever in Blue Jeans. In hindsight, the title of the Neil Diamond hit song seems to have been a long-term fashion forecast. Jeans' popularity and variety only seems to grow as the years pass. And that is a good. Denim, that traditional fabric from which jeans are made, had its origin as a tough fabric for sailor's clothes in the French city of Nimes. Denim remains supremely economical and durable. Companies that add some embellishment to their jeans such as rips, paint splatters or embroidery in strategic spots often charge hundreds of dollars for their jeans. But you can find good fitting, good quality jeans at reasonable prices from a multitude of sources. Jeans' special design construction stands up to hard wear. And nothing can turn the male head better than a well-shaped female back end in a properly fitting pair of jeans. It is hard to imagine any chic, modern wardrobe without at least one pair. Most women have several. Some have dozens. Jeans are a good fashion investment.

When I was a child, the local department store sold two brands of jeans: Levi's and Wranglers. All the jeans for sale were for men and boys. But in that farming and ranching area girls wore those made-for-males jeans for casual wear too. I couldn't. I was too fat.

Not long after I had shed my excess pounds, jeans became the hot fashion trend for women. I went out immediately and bought a pair that fit me just as tightly as the ones on the models in the fashion magazine ads. What fun to wear them! Especially with high heels as was the trend at the time.

In these decades since my first pair of designer jeans, we have seen other fashion trends come and go. Various brands and styles go in and out of the "must have" category, but some incarnation of jeans seems here to stay.

In his book *The Karl Lagerfeld Diet*, fashion designer Karl Lagerfeld explained what motivated him as an overweight man to lose 80 pounds was his desire to wear fashions that his previously portly body could not wear—at least without looking ridiculous. And what men's fashion do we see the now slim Karl Lagerfeld wearing in the photo on the cover of his book? A pair of tightly fitting jeans. Karl Lagerfeld, the legendary Paris fashion designer, and his book cover photo seem to define as well as anything the place that jeans have in our fashion life today.

Today we see jeans worn with everything from a tuxedo jacket on the formal end of the scale to a bikini top on the casual end. Jeans are versatile and, if they fit properly, comfortable. If you are on a tight budget, or live in an area of the country where the style of dress is casual, a pair of jeans is likely your *most* essential wardrobe essential.

Jeans are available in almost any color you can imagine. You have great choice here. What colors are the best for chic? Since I grew up in a farming and ranching community, blue jeans look like work clothes to me. But urban dwellers do not seem to have this prejudice and many of the styles favored by the fashionistas are blue.

With a dressy top, black jeans can look very classy, but with a T-shirt or tank top, they can also look casual. Whatever color jeans you choose, they should work with the essential shirts and other essential tops. Though it seems today that basic traditional blue jeans are considered a neutral. You see them worn with tops of every color and style.

Jeans look best on the slim. (Well, doesn't everything?) Huge waddling hips encased in tight jeans are not a pleasant sight. But there are such a variety of styles of jeans that, even if you are Chic-On-The-Way-To-Slim, you should be able to buy a pair that are designed to look good on your particular body shape. The top that you choose to wear with the jeans can play a crucial role in how chic you look. Choose these tops carefully. If you weigh more than you want, a top worn as overblouse is probably the best idea. For those who do not feel comfortable in jeans of any sort, a denim jeans skirt in a mid-calf or ankle-length is a possible alternative.

As for those tight, form-fitting designer jeans that slim women wear, perhaps jeans can serve the function for Chic-On-The-Way-To-Slim women that they did for Karl Lagerfeld: they will be the motivation to become slim.

CASUAL SHIRT

Sometimes you need a shirt.

Most of the time sweaters and knit tops will adequately do the job of covering the body from neck to waist for casual wear. But most women need one shirt that is not an elegant blouse, but something more casual with sleeves—and buttons down the front.

My own pick for a casual shirt is a cotton or cotton blend oxford cloth shirt. There are many other incarnations of that wonderful cloth cotton, so you do have a wide range of choices. A good quality shirt is a good investment. I have a white cotton man's dress shirt style Liz Claiborne shirt that I bought from a clearance rack for $14 about a decade ago. That shirt has seen a lot of wear and a lot of laundry, and the fabric looks prettier and feels softer than the day I bought it. That shirt would have been a bargain if I had paid full retail price or it. It was an ultra bargain at the price I paid. A well-made shirt in a quality cotton fabric will wear beautifully for years and year. The shirt will still look good when a knit top will have long before shown the effects of too many laundry sessions. A knit top will never have the crisp look of an ironed shirt.

Should your casual shirt be white? Not necessarily. White is classic, but there is much to be said for a colored casual shirt. For those who are short in height or are Chic-On-The-Way-To-Slim, a white top and a dark pants or skirt cut the body in half and make you look dumpy. A monochromatic color scheme is always the most slimming and the most lengthening. So there is much advantage in a shirt that is in the same color, or the same color but a shade or so lighter than the skirt or pants with which you intend to wear it.

Long sleeves look chic. And they can be rolled up when the weather turns warm. With rolled up sleeves and tied at the waist, a shirt makes a good light-weight cover up for certain age upper arms. Lately I have been seeing more shirts with three-quarter length sleeves made in lightweight solid cottons for summer. For covering upper arms, these are neater and cooler than rolled up sleeves.

KNIT TOPS

The genesis garment behind all these knit tops we wear is, of course, the T-shirt. And once upon a time, not so long ago, T-shirts were just underwear.

Then, actors Marlon Brando and James Dean (and others) changed that. At some point in the not very distant past, T-shirts for women metamorphosed from being baggy knit garments carrying a message that attested to your participation at some cultural event or devotion to some sports team to a body-hugging fashion indispensable. Today our choice in sleeve length, neck style, texture, and color of the knit tops we wear is enormous.

You need at least two knit tops, one long-sleeved and one with short or three-quarter length sleeves in your basis wardrobe. Most of us have many more.

To be chic, knit tops have to fit your body well, and the knit has to be reasonably good quality to stand up to laundering. Knit tops must also be the right length from shoulder to hem. Shop until you find one that fits properly around your bust and ends at the right spot on your hip—or looks right when tucked in your pants or skirt. To test for how well the shirt stands up to washing, launder the top, run it through the dryer and see if it still fits and still looks good. If so, you have made a good choice and you should remember the brand when stocking basics. For quality knit tops, I think it is worth the extra effort to always launder on cold with the shirt turned wrong side out and to dry carefully on the low setting. A little sizing sprayed on the inside before touching up with a warm (careful, not hot) iron can add to the chic.

Knit tops are a way that you can add the season's "in" color to your wardrobe with little expense. French women who are careful to incorporate the season's trendy color into their wardrobe use this technique. Since their wardrobes are small, by the end of the season, the trendy top has seen a lot of wear and is ready to be discarded or downgraded to wearing for gardening or other at-home work.

If you are short with a small bust, you may find that you need to shop the girls or teens departments to find properly fitting knit tops. Chic French women have been doing this for decades.

SCARF

Wearing a scarf is chic. Wearing a scarf is so-o-o French. You really do need at least one scarf in your wardrobe. Do you have to wear a Hermès scarf to be truly chic? No, certainly not.

Quite honestly, I do not own a Hermès. But I do have a number of beautiful scarves that I put to very good use to accessorize and extend my small wardrobe. Many—some hand-painted—were gifts from *Chic & Slim* readers. I take great pleasure in wearing these chic accents to my personal style.

One secret to making scarves an important element in your chic appearance is knowing how to fold and tie them in some stunning way for each outfit you accessorize with them. I have always depended on a scarf-tying booklet. When I wrote the original *Chic & Slim*, I had, in my personal library, such a booklet I had bought some decades before. This booklet had about as much aesthetic appeal as the user's manual that comes with a lawn mower. But its unartistic drawings did an adequate job showing several nice ways to tie various sized scarves.

Not long after I launched the *Chic & Slim* website, one of the readers sent me a lovely scarf tying booklet as a gift. Published by Nordstrom on heavy white card stock, the illustrations are elegant, and the directions clear. I keep it in my scarf drawer to refer to when I need a new idea or a refresher.

These days you can find instructions for scarf typing with an Internet search. There are even online how-to videos to view.

But you may not need to tie your scarf. French women, for whom simplicity is a science, very often take a 36-inch square scarf (the standard size for Hermès scarves) fold it into a triangle and drape the scarf over the shoulders of their blouse, sweater or jacket. They also often drape a long oblong scarf unfolded. No knot required. But I have always suspected that the draped scarf provides more opportunity for a viewer to recognize the scarf is, in fact, a real Hermès scarf than if it were folded and knotted. I also suspect that drape method works better in Paris than in North Texas where I live. Should I would walk outdoors with my scarf draped, not tied, most likely a gust of wind would blow off the plains, and my expensive Hermès scarf would be halfway to San Antonio before I knew it.

If you have no suitable scarves in your wardrobe, my first suggestion for acquiring an essential scarf is that you wait until you have your other *Chic & Slim* Essentials chosen before you go shopping. If you are making an investment of more than $15 or $20, it is a good idea to buy the scarf from a store that has a liberal return policy. Without removing the tags on the scarf, put on the outfit or outfits you plan to accessorize with it and lightly make a trial tie. (You don't want to badly wrinkle an item you might need to return. The store might not exchange it.) Look in the mirror. Is this the effect you want? Do the scarf and the other clothes work together? Does the scarf make you look chic?

For some of us who live in areas where the scarf selection is limited (largely to polyester), there are a number of online and catalog sources for scarves.

Some American women see scarf tying and wearing as a mysterious art, the secrets of which are only known to European women. This is not the case at all. But you are only asking for frustration if you buy a scarf and wait until 15 minutes before you must rush out the door to attempt an elegant knot. Learning to walk gracefully in high heels took some practice. Likewise, learning to tie and wear scarves takes a bit of practice too. Just think of scarves as high heels for your neck.

As a woman approaches certain age, scarves become more important as a fashion essential. A beautiful scarf at the neck can redirect a viewer's eye away from a face that is beginning to wrinkle and sag. Scarves also do a beautiful job of camouflaging neck crepe. French women put scarves to such marvelous chic use. You can too.

HAT

Hats. I adore hats. I love hats not only for their style possibilities, but for their very practical uses as well. Every chic wardrobe should have at least one hat. Of course, I love French berets!

When I was growing up, women wore hats for almost any activity that required a good dress. This even included downtown shopping in cities. In those days, women certainly wore hats for church. Girls too. Around the time I began elementary school, I stopped wearing bonnets with my Sunday dress and began wearing hats. Somehow a dressy ensemble was just not complete without a hat.

As a teenager, I observed that the more hairspray came into use, the less often women seemed to wear hats. Hairspray made possible the bouffant hairstyles that came into vogue. These viciously backcombed and lacquered hairstyles formed a sort of helmet that prompted one newspaper columnist to comment that a woman with such a hairstyle could quarterback for an entire football game and never have a hair out of place. With hairstyles that impervious, who needed a hat to protect one's hair and head from the elements? And how many hat styles worked well with bouffant hairstyles? Jacqueline Kennedy reportedly chose berets and pillbox hats that would sit toward the back of her head because these worked with her bouffant hairstyle.

The younger a woman, the more readily she gave up wearing hats, it seemed. My grandmother never gave up wearing hats, even after a number of her friends began to leave their blue-rinsed hair hatless. My grandmother would have been as likely to have attended a church service, a wedding, or a funeral without a hat as without her shoes. And, she, who died before the advent of sunscreen, was a strong advocate of sunbonnets.

For my grandmother and her friends who came to the Oklahoma frontier in the early 1900s, sunbonnets were a necessity to protect their faces from the sun as they went about various outside chores. By the 1950s, most of these women had given up sunbonnets. They no longer did much outside work, except for a little gardening in the early morning and late afternoon when the sun was not so fierce. But my grandmother kept her sunbonnet pattern. Every few years when the current one would begin to show signs of wear, she would buy fabric, cut and sew a new sunbonnet. If someone would pine for a sunbonnet like the one they used to have, they would be directed to my grandmother who would supply them with the pattern.

Sunbonnets were surely inspired by blinders for horses. The bonnet's sides extend well beyond the face. A wide sash secures it under the chin. The cloth of choice for my grandmother and her friends was a cotton print, a light-colored design on a white or cream background. Dark colors would absorb heat. The summer sun was hot enough without a fabric drawing heat to the head. The sunbonnet's brim that arched up the sides of the face and over the head required a stiffener, and the material of proper weight and stiffness my thrifty grandmother suggested was the cardboard that came with a man's new shirt.

While Scarlett O'Hara might have worn a wide-brimmed straw hat held in place by a ribbon under the chin, frontier women required a bonnet design that would better stand up to the prairie wind. So strong was my grandmother's belief in sunbonnets, that the summer I worked at the local swimming pool, she kept insisting that I should borrow her sunbonnet to wear while in the sun. Of course in those days, doctors were telling us sun was good for our skin, and tans were in. The last thing that I, or any other young person, wanted was a hat that would keep the sun off our faces. Besides what could look more ridiculous than a swimsuit and a sunbonnet?

A hat should make you look attractive, not ridiculous. We have sunscreens today, so we are not as dependent as our grandmothers on headgear to protect our faces. Though if you find that sunscreens and sunblocks clog your pores and cause breakouts, in some situations, a wide-brimmed hat may offer an alternative to cosmetic products.

Today hats' foremost job is to enhance chic. I like to think of a hat as the fashion equivalent of a tree top ornament for a Christmas tree: something special and decorative that sits at the highest point and makes the whole visually perfect.

You can buy new hats today. The selections are not what they were in the first half of the 20th century. Today we no longer see many shops exclusively dedicated to selling women's hats. Department store hat sections are not the large areas they once were. Some stores offer nothing beyond straw hats for sun protection and caps for head warmth. I have bought a number of vintage hats that I have found in collectibles shops and at garage sales. Hats hold up very well over the decades, especially if they have been stored in hat boxes. So when you find them at garage sales, they are often in amazingly good condition for their years. I have found great berets and cloches at garage sales. My favorite hat is a wide brimmed straw, vintage Neiman Marcus. That hat is great for wearing to summer weddings.

In certain age, some women find their hair thinning on top to the point that they almost have a bald spot. For women with this problem, hats can be an easy way to camouflage this detraction from their chic. Also in certain age, hair sometimes loses the luster it had in youth. A lovely hat can take a viewer's eye away from face and hair that may not be as glorious as they once were. Hats have a way of showing that maturity can still look splendid. Hats add a touch of class.

Hats can also come to the rescue when something interrupts a haircolor schedule. Your hairdresser has to have emergency surgery, or you are too exhausted to perform your regular haircolor ritual with an important event on the agenda. A visible half-inch of your natural hair running both sides of a top-of-the-head part looks unchic. Of course, if the re-growth is lighter than the color-treated hair, you can use one of those retouch pens to disguise your roots. But if the re-growth is darker than the color-treated hair, having a hat to wear may be the solution of choice.

You do not need a wardrobe of hats. One basic hat can do duty for a range of situations with small changes in decoration. Perhaps a different ribbon to circle the base of the crown, or attaching some feathers, or a pretty pin to the ribbon. One woman of my acquaintance was known for her frugality. She was invited to a niece's formal wedding and was unwilling to purchase a new hat for the occasion. At the same time, she did not believe that her old hat was sufficiently decorative. She caught a grasshopper. When the grasshopper was dead, she sprayed it with gold paint and attached it to her hat. I think I can safely say that no one else at the wedding had a hat exactly like hers.

Keeping the following points in mind when choosing hats will help ensure that a hat will make you look more chic, not less. Very wide brims do not work well on short, plump women. They can make them look dumpy. Yet a brimless or narrow-brimmed hat with a high crown can add height. Especially when worn with high heels, a hat can make a short, plump woman look taller and slimmer. Of course a high crown can make a tall woman look *very* tall. And very majestic. Think of that huge red hat that Sophia Loren wore in Robert Altman's film *Ready to Wear*.

One last—and obvious—advantage of hats: they keep not just your head, but all of you warmer. The French know that with a beret on your head and a scarf about your neck, unless the weather is extremely cold, you may not need to cover up your chic outfit with a bulky coat.

THOUGHTS ON QUALITY

Very likely, you will find that you already own most of the essentials on the basic *Chic & Slim* wardrobe list. Your planning will be for replacement items (even quality clothes do not last forever), or when a change in location or lifestyle puts new demands on your wardrobe. Whatever you buy, you want the best price for the quality you buy. Remember French women's emphasis on quality.

In France there has long been great emphasis on quality, especially in food and apparel—if not always in plumbing. That dedication to quality is not about to be discarded anytime soon, no matter how readily available cheap clothing becomes.

Reading *A Dash of Daring* Penelope Rowland's biography of Carmel Snow, I noted this comment in which Mrs. Snow, the editor-in-chief of *Harper's Bazaar* from 1934 until 1958, explains her love of Paris. She says: "I think it's because it's a place that worships quality, as I do. The best of everything. That, of course, is why Paris leads the world in fashion. Because the workmanship and the fabrics, as well as the designers, are the best that can be found. Because there's time for quality, because people care about quality. . . ."

Yes, the French do care about quality. And for French women that attitude pays rich dividends in helping them look chic. Quality is a wise clothing purchase guideline to follow wherever you live or shop. Certainly it is a wise guideline for acquiring the essential pieces that make up the foundation of your wardrobe.

So take your time. Look, evaluate, try on, compare. Remember all those items you cleaned out of your closet, those impulse buys, those things you could not pass up because they were on sale, those trendy pieces that were out of style almost before you drove home from the store? With a little planning, you can stop wasting your money on clothes that do not work for you and devote all of your clothing budget to pieces that give you good service and make you look very, very chic.

PERSONAL STYLE NOTEBOOK

One system that is useful to many women is a personal style notebook. Such a notebook can be your guidebook to chic. Years ago when I first began seriously developing my personal style, I used a spiral notebook, the kind students use to take lecture notes. Whenever I saw a good idea in a fashion magazine, newspaper ad or wherever, I cut it out and stapled or taped it to a page in the notebook. Often I made little notations of ideas in the notebook. Perhaps noting the store where I had seen a similar item or thoughts about colors or fabrics.

Later, I wanted more flexibility in arranging my notebook so I switched to a three-ring looseleaf binder. I invested in one of those three-hole punch gadgets. I would cut out pages from fashion magazines and other sources and punch holes in the pages and file them in the notebook in sections organized by seasons and clothing categories. (A ruler and a small boxcutter will facilitate a very neat cut of magazine pages.) By the time I visited the stores, made rounds of thrift shops, or poked around in garage sales, I had a good idea of the kind of look I wanted. I was better able to find bargains.

Here is another piece of advice: When you do venture out shopping, shop alone. The Parisian-born fashion designer Pauline Trigere also advised shopping alone. She said that you cannot trust the advice of even a "friend," because she might be jealous of you and give bad advice, or the friend's tastes might be so different from yours that the advice would not be useful to you. I agree with Pauline Trigere.

About twenty-five years ago, I went clothes shopping with a friend. Our tastes were totally opposite, and she almost drove me crazy insisting that I try on and buy dresses that I would no more have worn than I would have worn a plastic garbage bag. I vowed that forever after I would shop alone. And I have. With a few lovely exceptions such as the shopping my friend and I did after seeing the Corcoran's "Jacqueline Kennedy: The White House Years" exhibit. But on that shopping excursion I did lots of looking and no buying beyond some elegant note cards. My friend stocked basics at end-of-season clearance sales.

Véronique Vienne in her book *French Style* told us that French women do not buy overpriced basics. She writes: "French Style is good champagne, costly perfume, and a great haircut." But, she adds, for basics for casual wear, French women look for bargains. It is a good practice for all of us who are chic and thrifty.

BUY ONLY WHAT IS RIGHT FOR YOU
When shopping, be very, very finicky. Elegance is refusal, as fashion maven Diana Vreeland advised us. So is chic. If the piece isn't right for your personal style, don't buy. That right piece is out there somewhere. Just give yourself time to find it.

Until you find that what is right, wear what you have. And wear it with pizazz. Put what you already have together in a way that expresses the essence of you.

Remember that clothes are only one element in your personal style. A person with a well-defined style based on self-knowledge can put on almost any old thing (and tie a good scarf around her neck) and still manage to convince those who see her that she is chic. Style comes not so much from the season's ten top must-haves, as from a sense of self and an attitude of confidence. And do not neglect good posture. Elegant posture makes anything you wear look better than if you slump.

Some women anxiously scan the fashion magazines and look to celebrity photos for guidance as to what to put on their bodies. These sources do provide ideas, sometimes really great ideas. But just as French women do when they are look to others for style ideas, we should also consider who we are and consider whether these style ideas as we see exhibited by others would work well for us. Self-knowledge is a useful guide to style choices. When self-knowledge guides your personal style, and your personal style guides your clothing and accessory purchases, you are more likely to have and keep a slim armoire.

DEFINING TRUE STYLE

As Hara Estroff Marano, Editor-at-Large for *Psychology Today* magazine wrote in an article that appeared on the *eDiets* website:

> Style is a way of avoiding the clutter of stuff. It is a way of sorting through the crowded marketplaces, a way of selecting and a way of making choices influenced not so much by pressures such as advertising as by internal considerations. This kind of style no more requires change from season to season than does your character. But, neither is it completely static. Ideally, it should evolve over time, as character does.
>
> Style is self-knowledge applied selectively to the material world.

As I wrote at the beginning of this Armoire section, so many women have told me that cleaning out their closets and getting rid of the unwearable excess gave them a feeling of liberation. They told me that acquiring and maintaining a small, stylish, something-right-for-any-occasion wardrobe gives them a sense of serenity and confidence.

When you take control of your closet, you may find it easier to manage other parts of your life as well—especially eating. A slim armoire can be a means to chic style, but a slim armoire also can be a means to a slim body. And a slim body can be a potent asset to chic.

The Chic & Slim Boudoir

Relaxation for Chic & Slim

When a chic French woman feels stressed and exhausted, she often retires to her boudoir. A boudoir helps a French woman look chic and stay slim. || When an American woman feels stressed and exhausted, she will often push herself to keep going. She may eat a high sugar/high carbohydrate snack for a quick energy. Stress and exhaustion plus eating for energy and comfort adds calories that make it difficult for her to stay slim. || *This technique will show you how women, in the past, have used a French style boudoir to be chic and stay slim. It will also guide you in designing your own boudoir, or boudoir space, so that you too can enjoy great boudoir benefits.*

". . . to be left alone. And lock the door and find one's self again."

— Edna St. Vincent Millay

DECADES LATER, ANOTHER American writer Carolyn Heilbrun, quoting the American poet, expanded the idea: "to be alone, and then return after the solitude to love, to domestic duties, and to the comforting routine of the shared life."

In today's stressful world, even more than when Edna St. Vincent Millay penned those lines from her tranquil New England in the early 20th century, even more than when Carolyn Heilbrun expanded the thought while maintaining a busy schedule as university professor and novelist living in New York City in the late 20th century, women need a time when they can shut out the stresses and demands of their lives, when they can relax, rest, and find themselves again. This rest and self-rejuvenation requires a tranquil physical space in which they can reconnect with themselves. This restorative solitude helps to build defenses against mind-elsewhere eating and comfort food eating.

DEFINING THE BOUDOIR

Before we progress further, we should clear up possible misconceptions about the nature and purpose of the type of boudoir about which I am writing. If many Americans mistakenly think that the French boudoir is a place for carrying on illicit sexual affairs, there is good reason. By the 18th century, the French boudoir had evolved from its original design as a small, private room for a woman, to one that many French women used as their private little enclaves for promiscuity and amorous adventures. Confirmation of this comes from the best history of the French boudoir that I have found. That history is part of the introduction to *The French Woman's Bedroom* by Mary-Sargent Ladd. In this beautiful book, the author also assures us that many French women still maintain a boudoir, though the chief function today is solitude and relaxation.

The aim of this section is to guide you in creating a special space of your own where you can pamper yourself by partaking amply of those commodities so rare in today's life: solitude and relaxation. Your boudoir should be a place to de-stress.

FRENCH BOUDOIRS

My favorite writing about boudoirs appeared in the August 1992 issue of *Victoria* magazine. Author Judith Thurman, who was at that time living in Paris working on her biography of the French writer Colette, contributed a wonderful piece "A Boudoir of One's Own." She began the article addressing this problem of misconceptions about boudoirs telling the reader: "A boudoir is not, as romantic fiction would have us believe, a room in which a French countess, dressed in a muslin nightgown, plots the overthrow of a government with her wild-eyed lover."

Having established what a boudoir is not, Judith Thurman proceeds to describe the delightful boudoir of a French friend. "The Paris boudoir of my friend Madame P., for example, was once a dressing room. It has a tiny marble fireplace and French doors that open out onto a little balcony, where in warm weather a lemon tree blooms in a pot, and window boxes of primroses, ivy, and geranium spill over the wrought-iron railing." For relaxing, Madame P. has a "graceful daybed angled so it sits in the natural light." She has a cashmere throw draped over the side to cover her feet when she naps. Madame P. commissioned an artist friend to paint the ceiling with a watery abstraction in tones of rose, indigo, and gold to form a focus for meditation. The reader is assured that Madame P. spends a lot of time gazing at her ceiling.

When I first read Judith Thurman's description, I was struck that this delightful boudoir of her French friend is a tiny room. If you are preparing to abandon this technique because your living space would not spare even a small closet for a boudoir, stick with me. In any case, many of us will not have a room we can dedicate solely as a boudoir. We will have to use a room (or portion) that serves another purpose at least part of the time. As long as we can insure privacy for our boudoir time, this need not be a problem.

As for a boudoir's usefulness for weight control, Judith Thurman stresses that a boudoir and the "respectful self-indulgence" it provides is a form of nourishment. When a woman has nourishment from the comfort and pampering of a boudoir, she is less likely to look for nourishment from overeating. A decor that is a bit delicious will make it all more satisfying.

AMERICAN BOUDOIRS

The year in which I wrote the first version of this book, 2005, was a year in which several of my dreams came true. Unfortunately, my dreams came true for someone else.

One dream that came true for someone else was a house I dreamed of buying and restoring. At one point, it appeared the house was mine. But that was not to be. Someone else has had the joy of restoring the wonderful place to its former glory. One delight of this house was a room, set off in an alcove at the end of the master bedroom, a perfect little boudoir. In my mind I had already installed a *chaise longue* there with a tea table beside it, stocked the boudoir with favorite books and draped the windows. The boudoir would be a perfect place to curl up with a book and a pot of tea on a cold winter's day, or to close the shutters and luxuriate in the air-conditioning on a sweltering one.

Not surprising that in this 1926 house, built during an early 20th century Texas oil boom, the architect had included a boudoir. Such a room for the pleasure of the lady of the house was frequently found in upscale houses and luxury apartments in American cities in the late 19th and early 20th century. In the years when I was an avid reader of mysteries of the classic era, from time to time I would encounter a description of a boudoir of a luxury apartment or mansion. In Mary Roberts Rinehart's 1938 mystery *The Wall* there is a description of a boudoir in the New York apartment in which the victim had lived in late 1920s. We are told by Marcia, the story's narrator and the sister-in-law of the victim, that in this luxurious private lady's room there is a fireplace near a desk where Juliette took care of her correspondence. Then Marcia comments: "It had been an attractive room, jade-green curtains and mauve brocaded furniture as a background for her blond prettiness. Always before I had seen it filled with expensive flowers, silver photograph frames with pictures signed to her in terms of endearment, and the thousand and one trinkets with which she always cluttered her life."

A PLACE TO SULK OR POUT—EVEN GRIEVE

Boudoir takes its name from the French word *bouder* meaning to sulk or to pout. Thus, a boudoir is a room in which a woman can retreat in times of anger to sulk or pout and work out emotions out of the sight of others.

In that Mary Roberts Rinehart mystery novel from which I took the boudoir description, in a later chapter, the central character Marcia in a moment of justifiable frustration and anger writes, "I went into my room and had a private fit with the door locked."

French women are noted (and envied) for their serenity and the aura of calm self-control they project. A boudoir contributes to this aura in that the room gives women a place where they can go and do their pouting, sulking, or throwing an angry fit out of view of others. In public they can be all serenity and self-control.

Situations and people anger us. That is a reality of our world today. Bottling up anger can have a negative impact on our bodies. Research has found one common trait in cancer victims is a reluctance to express anger. Yet displays of anger have their negative side. Anger contorts the face and makes the voice shrill. Angry, a woman usually does not appear as attractive as when her face is relaxed and calm. When consumed by anger, it is difficult to think as clearly as when feeling more tranquil. Words spoken in anger are often regretted later.

Calm gives an aura of strength. But demonstrations of anger or frustration or exasperation send a message of weakness and lack of self-control. Having a place where we can go and have our "private fit with the door locked," and then, in that same private space, collect our thoughts and decide how to deal with the problem can be an advantage.

Many times, the best action for dealing a problem is no action: just ignore the incident and move on. But with no cooling off space, we might act on our natural desire for retaliation. Some people attempt to provoke us as a way of controlling us. So if a coworker baits you and you can remain calm, it can be to your advantage in dealing with that coworker. On the other hand, it can be disastrous to family life if you remain calm in dealing with the coworker, then take out your anger on your children, your husband, your partner, your dog, your neighbors, or even complete strangers who have the misfortune to cross your path.

A boudoir or boudoir space can provide a decompression chamber where angers, stresses and frustrations can be set aside or ignored—at least for a half hour or so. A boudoir is the perfect place to "get over" whatever is upsetting us. A distracting book, a comic film, some soothing music, a relaxation recording, a nap, doing something we enjoy such as embroidery or painting, doing nothing—any of these can help us regain our calm and take back control.

With technology available today, the reaction to an angering or stressful situation is too often phoning or texting a friend and unloading on them. Nothing is as exhausting and time-wasting as listening to someone wail and fume about a situation that upsets them. Certainly friends can be supportive when support is needed, but do them the courtesy of working past the first rush of emotion before you take their time to discuss your situation with them. In the first place they will be more sympathetic when you do not consume an undue amount of their time. In the second, having taken time to compose yourself, you will be in a more rational frame of mind to listen to helpful comments and advice they give you. Well…maybe.

People differ in the way they cope with grief. Some benefit from supportive contact with sympathetic friends and family. Others need solitude and quiet and a time apart in which to heal. A boudoir can provide the seclusion and privacy to heal in times of grief.

But whatever needs a boudoir meets, to have its full benefits, we must have possession and use. For periods of time, at least, a boudoir must be "a room of our own."

A ROOM OF ONE'S OWN

A room of one's own. We associate that phrase with the early 20th century British writer and critic Virginia Woolf. But in her definition of a room of one's own in her long 1929 essay by that title, she was defining what was required for a woman who wished to do creative work, specifically the work of writing. But what we are talking about here in this Boudoir technique is not so much creating a place to work, but more often a place to escape and recover from work.

Yet a room that would meet Virginia Woolf's requirement for "a room of one's own" for any kind of home office or workshop, if properly outfitted, could also serve as a boudoir. Several of my home offices have served both functions. Putting the cover on the typewriter (later putting the computer to sleep), setting out the tea tray with pretty china and teapot, putting myself in a comfortable seat with an interesting view, and opening a good book made the conversion of the room's function from work center to boudoir.

Writing more recent than Virginia Woolf's about a private nurturing space is Michael Pollan's A Place of One's Own. His book is the account of his project to build for himself (with the design and guidance of a gifted architect) a small office-in-the-woods on his New England farm. In his first chapter titled "A Room of One's Own," Michael Pollan asks who would not wish for "a place of solitude a few steps off the beaten path of life." He describes how he found the writings of the French 20th century philosopher Gaston Bachelard useful in thinking about what features his little private space would require to meet his needs. The book from which Michael Pollan quotes is Gaston Bachelard's 1958 book La poétique de l'espace translated into English as The Poetics of Space: The Classic Look At How We Experience Intimate Places. He quotes Bachelard: "If I were asked to name the chief benefits of the house, I should say: the house shelters daydreaming, the house protects the dreamer, the house allows one to dream in peace."

If you find this French intellectual's definition of a house curious, remember that, as I have pointed out in other Chic & Slim writings, for the French, their homes are their sanctuaries. Dropping by for an unplanned visit is not a French thing to do. In France, should someone be so rude as to show up at someone's home unexpected, they likely would not be invited inside.

In discussing Bachelard's theories, Michael Pollan reminds us that daydreaming does not rate highly in American culture. In the USA, daydreaming is most often seen as frivolous, an unproductive waste of time. But even the most Puritanical workaholic would have to admit that daydreaming is pleasurable.

Is daydreaming really so unproductive?

Michael Pollan also writes that in our daydreams we acquire a sense of what we are about. Most of us know from experience how good ideas and solutions to problems pop into our minds when we are thinking about something entirely different.

Gaston Bachelard's statement that the house is for sheltering daydreaming and for protecting the daydreamer so that they may dream in peace is an interesting idea, and one, I think, that has relevance for losing weight, staying slim, and maintaining our own personal style.

If we do not have a safe, private place in which to daydream, a place in which to come to an understanding of who we really are, then we are too likely to let the opinions of others define us. These definitions by others can be limiting—and damaging. These definitions by others can keep us from being as slim and as happy and as successful as we could be if we had time and a place to create our own definition of ourselves.

Gaston Bachelard's scholarly volume is not easy reading. But as I persevered through the pages, I came to understand that when the French philosopher says a house that provides shelter for daydreaming, this "house" could be any snug corner of a room, any cozy nook in a house or apartment. It could be your bedroom any time you could have solitude there. In a chapter of *The Poetics of Space* titled "Corners" the French philosopher writes: "Every corner in a house, every angle in a room, every inch of secluded space in which we like to hide, or withdraw into ourselves, is a symbol of solitude for the imagination."

Corners are havens. And we want our boudoir to be a haven, a sanctuary, and most of all, a place that gives us pleasure and freedom and an atmosphere for our creative ideas to ferment and grow. A boudoir must be our perfect pearly shell into which we can withdraw when we have the need. Bachelard quotes the French poet Noel Arnaud: "*Je suis l'espace où je suis.*" I am the space where I am. Our boudoir must be of us and for us.

THE INFLUENCE OF ELSIE DE WOLFE

A heyday of the boudoir in American homes and apartments was the late 19th and early 20th century. One of the strongest American influences on interior decor at this time was Elsie de Wolfe, a woman whose excellent taste set her on the road to her title as first woman interior decorator. She is credited with having created the profession. She certainly established interior decoration as a respectable and lucrative career for women. In 2004, Rizzoli reissued Elsie de Wolfe's 1913 classic *The House in Good Taste*. While Elsie de Wolfe's clients were the wealthy who could afford her steep fees, she saw the book as a way that she could share her decorating expertise with those of more modest means. The book devotes an entire chapter to the boudoir. The chapter title "Sitting Room and Boudoir" reflects the alternate name that those who wished to avoid the risqué connotation that boudoirs had earned in the 18th century. Elsie de Wolfe's introductory sentences clarify her meaning. She writes that a proper boudoir is the sitting room of a woman of many interests.

A sitting room of a woman of many interests. I like Elsie de Wolfe's definition. She wants to make clear that a boudoir is not just a bedroom or a dressing room, nor is it the preserve of some empty-headed woman. A boudoir is a room that serves a purpose for an intelligent woman who has a diversity of interests beyond her appearance and her wardrobe.

Elsie de Wolfe had absolutely nothing against attention to appearance and wardrobe. She was reported to have undergone four face lifts, was devoted to her exercise and diet regime, and in 1938, one of the Paris fashion groups named her "Best Dressed Woman in the World."

Elsie de Wolfe acknowledges the boudoir's French origin: "It began in old France as the private sitting room of the mistress of the house, a part of the bedroom suite, and it has evolved into a sort of office deluxe where the house mistress spends her precious mornings, plans the routine of her household for the day, writes her letters and so forth. The boudoir has a certain suggestion of intimacy because it is a personal and not a general room."

In the chapter, Elsie de Wolfe describes in detail four boudoirs. The first is a French boudoir that she observed in an old French house. She describes it as small, as was common in for 18th century French boudoirs.

About eight feet by eleven feet, yet it contained a fireplace over which hung a mirror. There were two windows, a day bed, a French lady's desk in the style known as *bonheur du jour*, daytime delight, behind which hung a floor to ceiling mirror, and two armchairs, and a small footstool. The mirrors and the very orderly arrangement of the furnishings of the room gave the suggestion that the room was actually larger than it was, she tells us.

The other three boudoirs Elsie de Wolfe describes in this chapter are her own, as well as the boudoirs of her friends Elisabeth Marbury and Anne Morgan, rooms decorated by Elsie de Wolfe. Perhaps because the decorator was one of the 14 women profiled in *The Power of Style: The Women Who Defined the Art of Living Well* in the 1994 book by Annette Tapert and Diana Edkins, we have a revived interest in Elsie de Wolfe.

The names Elisabeth Marbury and Anne Morgan are not as familiar today. But Elisabeth Marbury was the first woman literary and theatrical agent. She is credited by some with inventing the musical comedy. As Alfred Allan Lewis points out in *Ladies and Not-So-Gentle Women*, Elisabeth Marbury also made "a brilliant career on a taste for the dramatic verbal elegance of the French."

The boudoir concept was indirectly involved in launching Elisabeth Marbury's career. At that time *Feu Toupinel* was the hit play in Paris, she persuaded the author Alexandre Bisson to grant her the rights for a New York production. She intended to produce the play as a literal translation from the French. But in New York, she was told that the subject matter was too risqué for a Puritanical American audience of the 1890s. *Feu Toupinel* was what was known as a "boudoir farce." The plot revolved around a man who was caught deceiving both his wife and his mistress. American audiences would not tolerate a man who had both wife and mistress, Miss Marbury was told. So she changed the play. Americans would accept bigamy better than adultery. So she gave the character two wives and then had him die. The play that launched Elisabeth Marbury's career was *Mr. Wilkinson's Widows*.

Anne Tracy Morgan was the youngest child of the American financier J. P. Morgan. The heiress became an influential advocate for the rights of working women, and her administrative genius brought success to her World War I relief programs. At the time that *The House in Good Taste* was published, the three women were sharing and restoring the Villa Trianon, the charming early 19th century house in Versailles that was Elsie de Wolfe's home for 45 years.

In *Elsie de Wolfe: A Life in High Style*, her biographer Jane S. Smith mentions a large boudoir on the second floor of the Villa Trianon with its Savonnerie carpet profuse in flowers and scrolls, and richly striped wallpaper in Elsie's favorite shades of rose and green.

Elsie de Wolfe tells us her own boudoir is sitting room, library, and resting room combined. "In the early morning it is my office, where I plan the day's routine and consult the housekeepers. In the rare evenings when I may give myself up to solid comfort and a new book it becomes a haven of refuge after the business of the day. When I choose to work at home with my secretary, it is as businesslike place as my downtown office. It is a sort of room of all trades, and good for each of them."

If a boudoir serves the woman of the house, what about a room offering the advantages of a boudoir for the man of the house? Elsie de Wolfe, who did not marry until she was in her 60s, is sometimes criticized for ignoring the needs of men living in the homes she decorated.

In fact, Elsie de Wolfe believed that, in the Victorian interiors she found so oppressive and worked so hard to change, that men were too often treated as long-term guests rather than full-time residents. She did not like either the terms den or office, but she commented in the boudoir chapter that a man needed "a room of his own big enough to hold all his junk."

BOUDOIR READING

Books about the life of Elsie de Wolfe make excellent boudoir reading for those who have an interest in France and in a French-influenced lifestyle. Elsie de Wolfe's decorating style was definitely French, but her advice was designed to help Americans achieve French style in an American home. So many of her ideas were so thoroughly incorporated into American ways of decorating that many people today do not realize that these are Elsie de Wolfe's imported French ideas.

Jane S. Smith's biography *Elsie de Wolfe: A Life in High Style* published in 1982 is rich with details of the decorator's major projects. You can find a wealth of information on the discovery, purchase and restoration of her homes in the USA and the Villa Trianon in Versailles, as well as her Paris apartment. The Paris apartment became known for its large bathroom where Elsie de Wolfe served tea and gave cocktail parties. The book's preface is written by Diana Vreeland, herself a major force in American style in the 20th century. She calls the decorator a woman of "tremendous taste" and "tremendous chic."

In the prologue to the biography, Jane S. Smith writes: "Elsie's values were those of her beloved eighteenth-century France: a supreme respect for style, in conduct as in objects, and a conviction that artificiality can be a positive quality that celebrates the shaping power of imagination. But her personality was quintessentially modern and American: energetic, optimistic, self-created, and self-promoted."

For anyone interested in house restoration and decorating, or in creating and refining their personal style—or, for that matter, launching themselves in a career, there are good lessons reading about Elsie de Wolfe.

A later book that puts the life of the decorator in the perspective of her relationships with three other women also provides excellent information on her projects and style. Alfred Allan Lewis' 2000 book *Ladies and Not-So-Gentle Women: Elisabeth Marbury, Anne Morgan, Elsie de Wolfe, Anne Vanderbilt, and Their Times* weaves the stories of the three previously mentioned women with that of Anne Vanderbilt, another American woman who used her position, money, and influence to run a major war relief program in France during World War I and who started the first drug addiction treatment program in the USA.

All of these American women owned homes in France and spent much of their adult lives as residents of France.

Writing about these exceptional women, Alfred Allan Lewis comments: "They had dash, wit, intelligence, and industry. Without actually discovering anything new, they had the courage to transform much that was stagnant."

He uses industry in the sense of diligent activity toward a goal. Truly these women worked diligently toward finding solutions to problems and needs they saw around them. They created for themselves meaningful and satisfying lives. In taking responsibility for their own life and happiness, and in working to improve the lives of others less fortunate than themselves, these women, all born in the Victorian era, opened the career doors and role opportunities for other women at a time when these doors were largely closed.

Yet these women achieved their goals in their own feminine way. Not by demanding that some outside authority give them their "rights," but by going to work and doing what they believed needed to be done. Alfred Allan Lewis commented about their methodology: "Ingenuity and orderly change can also be tools of revolution."

In looking at these women's lives, you can see the influence of France and French culture as well as the methods of French women in the techniques these women employed in achieving their revolution. Surely their boudoirs served them well, not only a place for rest and restoration, but as an environment that fostered the creative thought that guided their work.

A PLACE FOR SERENITY AND CREATIVE THINKING

Our own boudoirs can serve us well as a place for our creative thinking —if we are clever about the way we design them.

Decor can distract from creativity, or it can enhanced it. Decor can give us a sense of peace and security—or it can upset us. We do become the space where we are. So how can we design our own boudoir or boudoir space to give us the best benefits the room can offer?

What furniture and other items are necessary to give us that comfort, privacy, rest and renewal we desire? If you can dedicate a room as a boudoir, that's *fantastique*. But even if you are only converting a portion of a room usually used for another purpose, there are four essentials for a boudoir space.

1) SOMETHING ON WHICH TO SIT OR RECLINE comfortably. You need comfort even if only a pillow against the wall while you sit on the floor. The proper chair is even better, especially if you can elevate your feet.

2) TABLE OR TRAY. Within arm's reach you need something on which to place such things as books, teacup, and decorator items. For those who are floor or bed sitters, a tray is surely more practical than a table.

3) MUSIC. The right music has wonderful power to soothe your soul, help you relax, and spur your creativity.

4) VIEW. Anything from a charming landscape or waterscape outside your window to a scenic postcard placed within your view can transport you to tranquility and inspire you.

SOMETHING ON WHICH TO SIT—PERHAPS TO DREAM

Looking at each necessary boudoir element individually, we start with the most important: something on which to sit or recline. Even if your boudoir budget is zero, you can usually designate a chair or a cushion for boudoir use. If you have a boudoir space instead of a dedicated room as your boudoir, you will find an advantage in choosing the same seating in the same location on a regular basis. You might need to change that location with a major change in season, however. The sun's angle through a window or the difficulty controlling temperature at a particular time of year. A porch that was delightful spring through autumn might be impossible in winter. The advantage in having the same seating for your boudoir each day is that you will come to associate that place with your time to relax and pamper yourself. Put yourself in that location and your subconscious will send your body a message to relax.

Say boudoir, and a *chaise longue* banked with cushions comes to mind. Not only can a *chaise longue* add elegance and luxury to your room, but the chair forces you to elevate legs and feet when you sit. That is good for circulation and is one way you can lessen your chances of developing unattractive broken and varicose veins on your legs. You can find these chairs in price ranges from a several hundred dollars to many thousand. When shopping for a *chaise longue* in the USA, the process can be complicated by terminology. Chaise longue, long chair in French, is often corrupted in the USA to chaise lounge. Looking at the words *longue* and lounge you can see how they lead to confusion, especially since one meaning of lounge is relax, something you could do in a *chaise longue*. So if you set out to find the *chaise longue* of your dreams, keep these possible terminological roadblocks in mind. For both space and price reasons, a chair and ottoman combination might be a better choice for many of us.

In your seating, you want a certain amount of elegance, but that can always be achieved with a throw and a couple of pretty cushions. Most important is comfort. If your current seating lacks sufficient comfort, probably the shortest and most economical route to comfort is with various decorator cushions and back supports you can buy. Sometimes used alone and sometimes in combination with special seat cushions, they can prevent the discomfort that sometimes comes with sitting.

Most likely you already own a piece of furniture that will work for your boudoir seating. But make sure that you optimize the comfort. A boudoir is for pampering and pleasure.

TABLE OR TRAY

Tables are not a luxury. Tables are a necessity. Once you have the matter of seating settled, you need to provide yourself with a table on which to place whatever else you might need to make your boudoir time enjoyable. If you don't have a table that seems appropriate, inexpensive tables or stands can be found at any discount store.

If you have a surplus of books, you can store your books and have a table by putting one of those round glass tabletops or a large tray on three or four stacks of books of equal height. If you need a book from one of the stacks, the other stacks of books will support the table top while you take out (and replace) the book you need. Getting all stacks of books the same height is the trick. You can find those round glass table tops at discount stores and in more upscale stores. This type of glass-topped table is *not* advisable for homes with active children or pets.

As an exercise in getting ideas for tables, sit down with a decorator magazine and turn through the pages focusing on the small occasional tables in each room photo. You will be surprised how many and what variety of these tables are part of modern decor.

Tables can hold memories and inspiration. If you have special souvenirs that remind you of happy times or of people who are particularly dear to you, or of plans you hope to achieve, your boudoir table can hold icons of these as well as the more practical items such as your teacup and reading glasses.

MUSIC

Music has the power to set or change our mood. Music can insulate us from distractions around us, especially if we use headphones for listening. Music can make our boudoir time even more relaxing and restorative.

A number of genres offer music that will provide good background music for your boudoir time. What pleases you and has meaning for you should guide your choices. For most of you, choosing the right music for listening during your boudoir time will be a simple matter of looking through your music collection and choosing what you find most soothing or inspirational.

A nice harmony comes from coordinating your music with your decor. For a modern minimalist boudoir, you might chose modern jazz. If you have an outdoor or porch setting for your boudoir, one of the pastoral symphonies might be appropriate.

Should you have a Biedermeier *chaise longue* for your boudoir, what better than some Schubert string quartets playing in the background? The Austrian composer Franz Schubert is associated with the Biedermeier period during which musical performances were often enjoyed in the home rather than in the concert hall.

Perhaps because a boudoir is such a French concept, and because French women put boudoirs to such good use, French classical music seems very appropriate for boudoir listening. Baroque, music composed between 1600 and 1750, offers many soothing compositions. French Baroque is often more delicate than music by many German and Italian composers of this era.

Choose the music that delights and soothes your soul.

A VIEW

A view is very important to me. As for many people, a tranquil natural scene brings me a sense of contented peace and centers me in the world.

Three different times I have lived in homes that gave me marvelous seascapes from my windows. Once the Atlantic, once a Gulf of Mexico bay, and the most spectacular: the Mediterranean.

Though I no longer live where my windows look out on water, I have a framed print of a Monet painting of the Mediterranean on my wall. I do not know precisely where the French Impressionist painter sat to paint this scene, but it is so exactly the view and the light on the water on sunny days that I remember. One glance at this picture and it brings all the color and sparkling, rippling water back to vivid memory.

Monet captured with his paint and brush a amazing likeness of the Mediterranean in sunlight I knew well, yet I was never able to capture as it so exactly with my camera lens.

Now, living far from the seacoast, I find contentment looking out at the back garden I have been restoring from the previous residents' neglect. The tranquil greenery with bright color from patio pots in summer and the coral berry bushes that provide brilliant magenta foliage along the fence in winter are as soothing as a good massage. The antics of the squirrels capering in the tree branches and the nonchalance of resident robins bobbing across the grass amuse and cheer me.

You can create your own lovely views, either faux or real.

Even if your window looks out on a brick wall, or even worse, the air-conditioning units of the next building, you can have a pleasant view. If you are artistic, you can paint a faux window on the wall. Or hire a painter to do the work. A large poster or a painting might supply a window-like view at a more moderate price than hiring a painter. That is, unless you can find a starving artist who is willing to work for starvation wages, or for just good home-cooked food.

For a view that can change at your slightest whim, you can simply buy a scenic calendar. The choices are extensive. Or, you can set out a postcard of a scene you like. I save postcards and scenic note cards that *Chic & Slim* readers and other friends have sent and use them as bookmarks. A glance puts me on a shopping street in England, a street of magnificent architecture in Prague, or a field of lavender in Provence. Many cards picture scenes of places that I, at one time, visited myself. In such cases, a card will bring a flood of mental images and memories.

DESIGNING YOUR BOUDOIR SPACE

Now that we have discussed the essential elements, time for the fun: designing your boudoir space.

Some of us carry our dream boudoirs in our heads: a montage of rooms we have seen in magazines, ideas collected from homes we have visited (or in which we previously lived), interiors we have seen in films, pages from catalogs, scenes in memorable books we have read.

For ideas, all the above-mentioned are great resources. You can sit down with a stack of these resources and drink in their ideas. You can clip pages and collect ideas in a three-ring binder as I often do.

Once you have a generous supply of ideas for your boudoir, it is time to dream. If you were designing the perfect place of your own, a retreat, a sanctuary, what would it be like? Forget practicality at this stage, just dream. Sometimes the manifestations of our dreams are more attainable than we think. Especially if you are as savvy about recycling the castoffs of others as I am. Valuing quality over trends is useful.

So dream for a time about your boudoir. If you find it helpful for the design process, you can try brainstorming your ideas. For brainstorming, I usually use a kitchen timer set for 10 to 20 minutes. I write with pen, or on the computer. Other times I go for a more visual approach sketching with colored markers on a large sheet of paper. Still other times, I use scissors and a glue stick and cut and paste together a collage of ideas from my magazine and catalog clippings. I use whatever works best at that moment to spur my creativity.

Some people construct a complete plan of a finished room and work from that. I prefer the gradual approach to decorating. In the long run, I achieve more pleasing results. I am not so likely to be forced to choose between living with something I don't like much and the equally unappealing process of redoing. Recently a friend was showing me the interior of a charming brick 1920s Tudor she is redecorating. She apologized that the dining room in which we were standing was still a work-in-progress. I mentioned that I thought that the end results were better when you decorated incrementally. Do part of the work, live with the room a while, and then decide where you want to go from there. She agreed, "If I had gone ahead and done everything as I initially planned it, I would have been unhappy with the results. After I painted the walls this dark color, I saw that some of the things I planned would not look the way I originally thought they would."

The gradual approach is one French women use for both their personal style and the decor of their living spaces. The system generally brings them admirable results.

GOALS, NOT RULES

There are no rules in designing a boudoir. But there are goals. You want your boudoir to make you comfortable. You want your boudoir to make you feel safe and snug and protected from the pressures that stress you. You want your boudoir to bring you a sense of peace and tranquility. After spending time in your boudoir, you want to feel stronger and capable of coping with whatever comes your way. You want to believe that you can handle whatever confronts you.

A century ago, if we had we set about organizing a boudoir or boudoir space for ourselves, we might have looked to Elsie de Wolfe for design guidance. While many of the interior decorator's ideas are usable today (as we discussed earlier in the chapter), her aim to transpose the interiors of 18th century France to 20th century American houses and apartments may not work well for the 21st century lifestyles of many today. We want elegance. But we want casual, livable elegance that leaves us time for leisure. Most of us do not have Elsie's battalion of household servants.

Barbara Barry is an American designer who in the past two decades has built a devoted following for both her interiors and for the furniture and accessories that she has designed. Her design philosophy aims at achieving both elegance and livability.

Barbara Barry writes:

It's not how much we have
    but how the things we have enhance our lives.
Simplicity is a discipline.
I believe in the power of design to transform lives.

Simplicity is the discipline that guides French women in their personal style as well as in arranging their living spaces. French women do not aim to have a great number of possessions. They aim to have the right things that enhance their lives with convenience and pleasure.

Simplicity. Elegance. Tranquility. These are our boudoir design goals.

Design does have power to transform lives. Our design will determine the extent of our boudoir's power to transform us into the chic, slim, happy and successful individuals we wish to be.

The Chic & Slim Cuisine

Kitchen Organization for Chic & Slim

Chic French women shop daily or almost-daily for food that will be consumed at meals that day or the next. They do not keep large quantities of food on hand. Little food is available for snacking. || Americans buy more food than their household could possibly consume. Much of this excess is high-calorie convenience food whose overconsumption contributes to excess weight and even obesity. || *This technique guides you in reducing the amount of food you keep on hand, especially junk food that can make you fat and unhealthy. Then, it guides you in designing a Slim Pantry to keep you chic and slim and healthy.*

PAS BEAUCOUP. NOT MUCH. If the amount of food you have in your pantry and your refrigerator is not much, you will be less likely to overeat when you have an attack of hunger, whether it is real or only mind hunger. If you have a supply of healthy, nutritious, easily prepared food on hand, when you are too tired, too depressed, or too rushed to prepare a regular meal, you will be more likely to eat healthy food that will keep you slim.

Theory simple. Practice a bit more tricky. *Non?*

In his book *Low Fat Lies, High Fat Frauds, and the healthiest diet in the world*, Dr. Kevin Vigilante writes: "If it's not in the house, not visible, or out of reach, you won't eat it. So the first step in an effective diet (defined as habitual way of eating, not as a temporary regime) is to keep the right stuff in your house and the wrong stuff out." He advises you to remove junk food from your cupboards and banish fast food from your life.

I often see kitchens of Americans who live a mile or less from a supermarket and who shop at least every two or three days, yet who keep on hand enough food to feed a village in Africa for a week. Much of this excess food Americans stock in their refrigerators, freezers, and pantries is high in calories and low in nutrition; much is unhealthy: highly processed and containing undesirable chemicals and additives.

Organizing your kitchen and pantry for *Chic & Slim* involves two steps. First, this section offers a plan for reducing excess food and undesirable food, both likely to make or keep you overweight. This is the Clean Out for Slim step. Second, this technique gives you a suggested list of foods from which you can design your own Slim Pantry. This is the Stock for Slim step.

Eating is not like smoking, or any number of other unhealthy habits. You cannot just quit.

You must eat to stay alive. You must eat healthy foods in a reasonable, moderate manner to stay healthy and slim. Somewhere between the very healthy, but devoid of pleasure eating regimes advised by ultra-nutritionists and, at the other extreme, a junk and fast food dependence, there is a sensible, moderate way of eating that gives both a slim, healthy body and eating pleasure.

What you have and do not have in your cupboard and refrigerator can make a huge difference in how easily you stay slim.

The reality: as busy as most of us are, we often do not have the time or energy to spend much time in the kitchen. We must take preparatory steps if we want to avoid those times when, too exhausted to cook, we might stand at the counter eating crackers from the box, or call for the delivery of a pizza.

How wonderful if we could just copy the French/European model for keeping a small amount of food on hand and, three to five times a week, shop for a small amount of fresh, quality food. For a variety of reasons, including distance from food sources or time limitations, many of us in many locations in the USA cannot copy this model exactly.

NEGATIVE FORCES AGAINST HEALTHY EATING

In the USA, strong negative forces work against healthy eating. These forces do not exist in the same strength in France and other countries in Europe—at least not yet. But, sadly, they are getting stronger.

Our system for keeping a Slim Pantry must take into consideration the need for defenses against negative forces. You who have read the previous *Chic & Slim* books have already reduced the amount of food you keep on hand and organized your slim pantries. You have emailed to tell me of the successes and satisfactions these efforts have brought. But we live in a different world than the one in which I published the original *Chic & Slim* in 1997. In this chapter you will find useful new information to make your Slim Kitchen and Pantry more practical today.

Why do most Americans keep large quantities of food on hand? Some try to explain this practice with biological and historical reasons. They point out that, until very recent times, stockpiling food was necessary to survive famines. The more one stockpiled, the better one's chance of survival. They also argue that the trauma of hunger suffered by our parents and grandparents during the Great Depression left them a fear of hunger. Large quantities of food in the house makes them feel secure. They passed on to their children this habit of keeping much food on hand. But the ancestors of the French also had to stockpile food against famine. Many French who rarely have on hand more than enough food for one or two meals experienced near starvation during World War II.

A better explanation for the American habit of keeping large quantities of food in the house is the difference in French and American marketing techniques. You go to a French market and find there piles of fruit and vegetables along with a mini-chalkboard or a piece of cardboard on which the price is written. If you are a regular customer, you might be given the best produce available. But the French government limits when and under what circumstances sale prices can be offered. Food prices are regulated.

In the USA, for my whole shopping memory, few groceries and

supermarkets simply listed the price. The signs and announcements that greet one inevitably carry messages such as: 20% off! Stock up and save! Buy two, get one at half price. Additionally magazine articles have long advised smart shoppers: Never, never pay full price and buy only when items are on sale. Buying only when an item is on sale is good advice, as far as it goes. But if you stock up and save on four products one week, and four more products the following week, and you go out for dinner two nights this week, soon you have a *lot* of excess food on hand. And, if you are like many people, you will begin feeling pressure from this available excess to overeat. On the other hand, if you limit the quantity of food in your house, you will feel a pressure to eat less.

Paring down the amount of food on hand is a good idea. But *attention!* There are pitfalls to avoid in your paring down process. When you read that the French keep only a small amount of food on hand, your reaction might be open the cupboards and the refrigerator and toss everything except enough food for two days. For about a dozen reasons, this is a very bad idea. It is an especially bad idea if other family members are not in total agreement with your campaign and if it purges their favorite snack food. You could find yourself living in a house with some very unhappy people. In extreme cases, you might find yourself living in a house from which some very unhappy people have moved out.

When you begin your process to Clean Out for Slim, there are, however, several categories of foods it would be advisable to put directly into the trash. First on this throw-out list would be any foods that are spoiled or possibly spoiled. (Who really wants to take chances?) You should also toss frozen items that have resided so long in the depths of the freezer that they are beyond identification. Items that are past their expiration date should also go. Sometimes, I am visiting someone's home and helping them with meal preparation or cleanup and I notice in their cupboard some unopened bottle or can whose label is faded and yellowed. I check the expiration date and find the date is some three or four years in the past. Good grief! What is the point of keeping this stuff? Sentimental value? Why would one feel sentimental about a can of peas?

Another group of items that should go directly into the trash is any product that lists as a main ingredient high fructose corn syrup. (Actually I never buy any product that contains *any* high fructose corn syrup.) My opposition to packaged dry breakfast cereal is perhaps an irrational quirk given that my opposition extends beyond sugared cereals to even the more healthy ones. (Boxed dry breakfast cereal is not chic, says Anne Barone.) But my opposition to any product made with high fructose corn syrup is grounded in good medical science. If you want to eat a sugared dessert, eat a luscious chocolate éclair or a wedge of blueberry pie made with sugar. The negative effect on your body from plain old cane or beet sugar is less than that frankenfood, high fructose corn syrup. High fructose corn syrup I avoid as I do *e.coli,* salmonella, and botulism.

(Oh dear! The above was a strong statement. Do you think an ADM hit team is on the way?)

Once you have cleared out unsafe or potentially unsafe food, you have a couple of options for dealing with the rest of the excess. The first is the quickest and easiest. The second is the most economical and offers the most opportunities for creativity. But skip the non-options.

One non-option is throwing away the excess. With the extent of poverty and hunger in the USA today, it is simply wrong to throw away safe, edible food in unopened packages. The US Census Bureau statistics for Americans living in poverty in 2014 is 45 million. Inexcusable for a developed country such as the USA.

The most desirable, easiest, and quickest option is to box the excess food items and donate them to a food bank or church food closet. Some organizations have facilities for taking frozen items as well as canned and boxed. Besides food distribution organizations, you may have a family in your community that is struggling to make their income stretch for monthly expenses. Or you might know an elderly person whose pension no longer covers more than the most basic necessities. Extra food might reduce some of their worry about how they will pay their heating bill next winter or allow them to enjoy an extra hour or two of air-conditioning in the sweltering summer.

THE MOST ECONOMICAL OPTION

The most economical option for achieving a Slim Pantry, one that offers the most opportunities for creativity, is incorporating as many excess items as possible into your daily meals until you have reduced the excess to an acceptable level.

Say, for instance, one item you unearth from the back of your cupboard is a jar of kumquats in syrup. You had seen flaming French crepes with a walnut and kumquat filling prepared on your favorite cooking show and decided that you wanted to make those crepes. But, by the time you returned home from shopping, your five-year-old was running a 103 degree temperature and throwing up her lunch. After an emergency trip to the pediatrician and two nights with little sleep caring for a sick child, you lost your desire for flaming French crepes. So you grab your favorite cookbook from the shelf and look up kumquats. You think a kumquat sorbet sounds simpler and more to your taste in the warm summer weather. Or you might type kumquat into an Internet search engine and see what comes up.

Another way to use a search engine to rid your cupboard of excess is give the search engine names of two (or more) different items you have on hand and see what recipes it finds. This can give you interesting— and delicious—results

KEEP YOUR GOAL IN MIND

Whatever option you choose for paring down excess food, keep in mind that the goal is not only to reduce the amount of food. You also aim to set up a Slim Pantry so that you always have healthy food on hand. Then, if bad weather, or an illness, or simply lack of time keeps you from shopping and cooking for a few days, you will not find yourself eating food that might add extra fat.

Years ago, living in an apartment alone, I became ill during a snowstorm. I had not yet learned chic French techniques for staying slim, and unprepared for being housebound, I ate what I had on hand. For several days my meals consisted of tuna canned in olive oil, saltine crackers, cookies and a box of homemade fudge my mother had sent. As you can imagine, I gained several pounds in a few days. You want to avoid such situations.

Once you have eliminated the excess, it is time to set up your Slim Pantry.

CHIC & SLIM PANTRY

Those of you who have read other *Chic & Slim* books or followed the *Chic & Slim* website know that I resist giving menu plans or absolute rules. Why? Because I believe that menus and rules are things that keep diets from working both short and long term. So I strive instead to give you a *Chic & Slim* philosophy and examples from which you can create your own menus and rules uniquely designed for you.

I use that same approach with guidelines for a Slim Pantry. To help you design your own, I shall list what I keep on hand in my Slim Pantry. But this list is intended only as *inspiration*. And I will tell you that, though I had opportunities to see what chic French women kept on hand in their kitchens, I never tried to stock exactly the same items. Instead I used my observations as inspiration to design my own Slim Kitchen and Pantry.

Like my personal style, through the years my Slim Pantry has evolved and changed. Not only have the items varied through the years, but the amount I stock has also varied. Lately I have been keeping more food on hand than previously. Several factors have contributed to this. From my current home, I must drive to food shopping. For most efficient use of my time and fuel, once-a-week or every week and a half shopping works best, unless I happen to be near a food store while I am running other errands.

Another reason I now keep more food on hand is that some items I find necessary for the *Chic & Slim* lifestyle are not available locally. This means stocking up during out-of-town shopping trips or ordering. Security is also a consideration. Today in the USA we need to keep emergency food supplies on hand in case a natural or man-made disaster interrupts our access to food or makes evacuation necessary.

In previous *Chic & Slim* writing, I have explained how the limited amount of cabinet space and smaller refrigerators common in French homes help keep French women slim: less food on hand, less food that is available to eat, as well as less suggestion to eat by the presence of excess food. Conversely, in American homes, generous cabinet space and large refrigerators and freezers are often an encouragement to keep an excess of food on hand. Very often that excess leads to overeating.

But just because I moved to a house with a larger refrigerator/freezer and more cupboards, I did not feel compelled to stock food beyond an amount necessary and desirable for healthy eating. But I do find it convenient having refrigerator space to store an adequate supply of fresh fruits and vegetables, especially since fresh produce is an important part of my daily menus.

I also enjoy having more space for storing china and cookware. I cook almost everything "from scratch." I use good china and silver everyday—though I did not when my son was growing up. More utilitarian pottery and stainless steel tableware made more sense for everyday use in those days. From-scratch cooking and more formal dining require space for all the china and cooking utensils used on a daily basis.

STOCKING FOR SLIM GOALS
In Stocking for Slim, you have two goals. Your first goal is having sufficient quantity of the right foods on hand so that you can eat healthy foods that taste good on a daily basis.

Your second goal is having foods available so that when you are hungry but short on time and energy, you can prepare a healthy meal quickly and easily. Following is my Slim Pantry inventory. The list is grouped by location. You will note that, for some items, I have listed specific brands. Of course, there are other acceptable brands, many of them no doubt superior. Some items for which I indicate my brand preference are old favorites such as SAF yeast and Maille mustard, products that I discovered in French stores decades ago. They are excellent products—even if my preference for them is based on nostalgia. Others brands indicated are ones that I find acceptable from the somewhat limited supply I have available in my area. If you are looking for brand suggestions in any of these categories, you might try these brands as a starting point. If they do not suit you, try other brands.

Following the lists for some locations, I have added comments on my choices for my *Chic & Slim* Kitchen and Pantry.

Chic & Slim Refrigerator

2 to 5 kinds of fresh vegetables
2 to 3 kinds of fresh fruits
Fresh lemons and limes
Lettuce
Eggs, free range if possible
Milk, organic if possible
Canola oil
Yogurt, often homemade
Tofu
Feta or mozzarella
Butter
Flaxseed Oil
Prunes
All-fruit preserves
Maille mustard
Sweet mango chutney
Soy sauce or organic tamari sauce
Salsa
Tahini
2 Liters water

Note that first on the list are vegetables and fruits. I might run out of other items and simply do without until next shopping. But if I run out of fruit or vegetables, I go shopping for these basics of my healthy, slim eating. I try to keep fresh lemons and limes on hand. Lemons and limes add flavor and vitamin C at almost no calories to vegetables, fruits, as well as meats. One of my favorite meals is pan-grilled chicken breast and steamed green beans both generously anointed immediately before serving with fresh lemon juice. With a little sea salt and course ground black pepper, this is a wonderful, easy meal. If I am especially hungry, I serve the chicken and green beans with brown rice. Deglazing the pan in which I cooked the chicken breast with lemon juice and then pouring the liquid over the meat and green beans is also tasty.

Unless we find ourselves a period when lettuce costs more per pound than prime rib, I keep Romaine, Boston, leafy green, or leafy red lettuce on hand. Eating a salad course, as the French do, following the main course makes a moderate main course portion more satisfying. The French also claim it aids with digestion. In summer, I lunch almost every day on a salad of some sort. The variety of salads one can prepare is endless. Sometimes I prepare old favorites such as *Salade Niçoise*. (This tuna salad can be found in almost any French cookbook.) Other times I take inspiration from a new recipe in the newspaper or a magazine and make my own version based on what I have on hand and my taste preferences. And, of course, on what fits within my budget.

The French concoct wonderful meals around eggs. One of the best things the French do with eggs is make omelettes. An omelette is a favorite quick meal. If you do not know how to make a proper omelette, find a copy of a cookbook by Julia Child or another French chef and learn how to make a good French omelette. And, yes, you really do need an omelette pan. But acceptable ones are available at reasonable prices.

I find definite health benefits to a tablespoon of flaxseed oil a day. One day when I had no butter on hand, I decided to try flaxseed oil on my breakfast bread. Great nutty flavor.

Salsa will jazz up almost any bland food. You can add taste to beans, chicken, fish, or eggs without adding a lot of calories. And I could not imagine eating curry without a little sweet mango chutney. My current favorite mango chutney is Patak's Major Grey Chutney. It tastes like the chutneys I bought in my little neighborhood store in New Delhi, India.

Chic & Slim Freezer

1 package spinach
1 package green beans
2 packages other frozen vegetables
1 package fruit, often home-frozen
1/2 cup plain yogurt
1 package fish, uncooked
1 package cooked meat or fish
1 container homemade soup
SAF Yeast
Bread, whole grain
Barone breakfast bread
Muffins or teacake
Corn tortillas
Flour tortillas
Decaf whole bean coffee
Regular whole bean coffee

I keep extra thin corn tortillas on hand in the freezer for migas. But the flour tortillas I stock make an easy substitute for pizza dough. For lunch I often enjoy a Florentine pizza made with flour tortillas, cooked spinach, minced onions and garlic, olive oil and mozzarella cheese. You can substitute feta for the mozzarella, but it will not have as much of the conventional pizza taste. But Valbreso sheep's milk feta imported from France I have been buying does nicely here.

There are no tomatoes in this version of pizza. I was skeptical when a friend married to an Italian suggested I try it. But after I tasted Florentine pizza, I loved this tomato-less version. This pizza is easy to prepare in a toaster oven. Oil the tortilla on both sides and bake it in an oiled pan about five minutes at 425 degrees F. before you top with the other ingredients and return the pizza to the oven to finish cooking and melt the cheese. In my toaster oven that is usually another five or ten minutes.

I prefer SAF, the French yeast, for bread baking. I order it from the King Arthur Flour catalog and buy two one-pound packages at a time and keep it in the freezer for maximum freshness. The half cup yogurt I keep in the freezer is for starter for homemade yogurt, if needed. Yogurt that has not been frozen is preferable for making a new batch. But in case I run out, I keep that small amount frozen so I will always be able to make yogurt. Yogurt that has been frozen will work as a starter for a new batch if allowed to thaw in the refrigerator or on the counter top. Years ago my gynecologist recommended eating at least a tablespoon of yogurt with live cultures each day. I have followed the advice with good results. In winter months, soup is my frequent lunch. Just before serving, I often add two tablespoons to 1/4 cup yogurt to my hot soup for a creamy flavor. Sometimes I also add a tablespoon of brewer's yeast for protein, potassium, and B vitamins.

For me it is easy to prepare meat or fish for two meals, one to eat and one to freeze. I try to keep one meal's worth of cooked meat on hand for those days that I am hungry, but too tired or too busy to cook. The same process works with homemade soup, though with soup I can easily make a large batch and freeze several extra servings. Home-baked bread does not stay fresh for more than a day or two without freezing. After baking, I usually put a day's worth in the bread box and freeze the rest.

When I bake a cake or batch of muffins, I freeze what I do not eat immediately. One teacake that I have been making lately is made with prunes. Prunes are dried plums, after all, and their taste goes very well with tea. When I finally decided my fatigue was due to low potassium, I began to look for ways to incorporate foods rich in this necessary mineral into my daily menus. The prune teacake has several ingredients that are high in potassium, including prunes, oranges, bananas and blackstrap molasses.

Chic & Slim PRUNE TEACAKE

1/2 cup whole wheat flour	1/2 cup unbleached flour
3 teaspoons baking powder	1/2 teaspoon baking soda
1 teaspoon cinnamon	1/2 teaspoon ginger
1 cup pitted prunes	1 ripe banana
3/4 cup milk	1 egg
2 Tablespoons molasses	1/4 cup orange juice
1 teaspoon orange peel	1 cup rolled oats

Preheat the oven to 400 degrees F. Put all dry ingredients except oats, in a mixing bowl and stir. Put prunes, banana, milk, molasses, peel and egg in a blender or food processor and puree. Add orange juice and oats and puree. Pour the pureed wet ingredients over the dry and stir gently until moistened. Put the mixture into an oiled 10-inch diameter round fluted gateau pan (or other round pan or 12 muffin tins) and bake about 30 minutes, or until a wooden toothpick inserted into the center comes out clean. Cool in the pan 5 minutes before cutting. Store extra teacake in refrigerator or freezer. Plain yogurt make a healthy topping.

For years I resisted trying tahini, sesame seed paste. Finally I tried it, and loved the taste. Now I buy it regularly. A favorite use for tahini is in a dip for fresh vegetables.

The background story for this dip is a party to which I was invited several decades ago. The event was an engagement party for a friend who had recently become betrothed to a very pleasant young man from one of those countries whose geography is a great deal of sand underneath which lies a great deal of oil. I forget precisely which country. In any case, some time after the party, but before the wedding, which—as far as I know—never took place, it became apparent that the prospective bridegroom's family would expect my friend to wear a burka. My friend was definitely into mini-skirts.

But the night of the party, food, not wardrobe, was the focus. And the food was superb. I particularly enjoyed an eggplant dip that was served, and I made it a point to get the recipe.

The dip I discovered at my friend's engagement party is more nutritious and better tasting than most into which I have dipped raw vegetables. I also think that the French have a much better word for eggplant than Americans. *Aubergine* is one of those delicious French words that does justice to this beautiful vegetable.

Chic & Slim AUBERGINE DIP
> 1 medium eggplant (about 1 1/2 pounds)
>
> 2 Tablespoons tahini   2 cloves garlic (minced)
>
> 2 Tablespoons almonds finely chopped
>
> 1/2 teaspoon salt, or more to taste
>
> 2 Tablespoons chopped parsley leaves plus extra for garnish
>
> Juice of 2 medium lemons   Olive oil

Preheat the oven to 400 degrees F. Pierce the eggplant with a fork, place on a glass baking dish and bake for about 20 minutes or until very soft. The eggplant will deflate somewhat. (You can also cook in microwave about 15 minutes on high, but the dip flavor will not be as good.) Cool the cooked eggplant.

Scrape the flesh from the eggplant into a bowl. Discard skin. Chop and mash the eggplant flesh. Stir in the other ingredients adding the lemon juice last. Garnish with extra parsley and sprinkle olive oil over the surface of the dip. Cover and refrigerate at least 2 hours. Serve at room temperature for best flavor.

Chic & Slim Bread Box
> Whole grain home-baked bread
>
> Barone breakfast bread

Home-baked bread is best if left at room temperature rather than refrigerated. Home-baked bread keeps fresh for a day or so depending on the ingredients and method of baking. Bread stays equally fresh in a plain paper bag, the kind in which good bakeries put your purchase. Storing homemade bread in a plastic bag is not advised.

Chic & Slim Cupboard

  Extra virgin olive oil
  Balsamic vinegar
  Red wine vinegar
  Brown rice, organic, Texmati or basmati
  Lentils
  Black Beans
  Garbanzos (chick peas)
  Organic millet
  1 can tomatoes (whole or diced)
  Bouillon cubes
  1 can tomato paste
  1 can crushed pineapple (unsweetened)
  1 can tuna
  1 jar nopalitos (cactus pads)
  Stevia, powdered
  Stevia, liquid

I love lentils. Lentils are *so* French. The French have wonderful recipes for lentils with chicken and vegetables. One recipe that I clipped years ago from a French magazine combines onions, carrots, turnips and garlic with the chicken and lentils (and water.) These ingredients are baked slowly (about 325 degrees F. for several hours) in the oven for a hearty winter meal. Efficient French homemakers plans meals for two different days around chicken and lentils. The first day the chicken, vegetables and lentils are eaten as an entrée. For the second day's meal, more water is added to the remaining chicken, vegetables and lentils to make a soup for a lighter meal eaten with bread and cheese.

I keep garbanzo beans, also called chick peas, on hand for making couscous. Garbanzo beans are also great for humus or tossing in a salad. In the south of France, garbanzos are ground into flour for a thin pancake called Socca, of which I have become very fond. Socca is the only food I know that tastes best when you burn it a little around the edges.

An early French lesson I learned was the importance of stock in the cuisine. A big pot simmering on the stove to make chicken, beef, fish or vegetable stock was frequently to be found in a French kitchen. The French do make wonderful stocks for soup. But an interesting little secret I discovered was, that for making soup for supper at home, French women were likely to use a bouillon cube or two in place of long-simmered stock. Really.

The chic French women's quick version of French Onion Soup substitutes bouillon cubes dissolved in water in place of stock, though I do not think that the bouillon cubes sold in the USA in my supermarkets today are as flavorful as those I remember buying in French stores. The ingredients in today's bouillon cubes seem to be principally salt, sugar, and MSG. Still, French onion soup is an ideal soup for a chilly evening. With some French bread and red wine, you almost think you are in Paris. If you have no stock on hand, either canned or homemade, just substitute bouillon cubes dissolved in water for the stock called for in the soup recipe.

The jar of nopalitos I keep on hand is for making migas. Once, just once, in spring, I gathered the tender new cactus pads and peeled them for my migas. Never again. Peeling cactus pads (nopalitos), like making radish roses, is a tedious activity that I do not have time for in my life. When I want migas, I buy a jar of the nopalitos. My favorite brand is San Marcos, canned in Mexico. A warning: some jars of commercial nopalitos also contain serrano peppers. If you do not care for hot peppers, check the label to make certain the jar does not contain them.

Wire or Wicker Basket

Garlic

Yellow onions

Ginger root

I could not cook without garlic, yellow onions (said to be healthiest), and ginger root. Tofu and vegetable stir fry seasoned with minced garlic, grated ginger root, and soy sauce is an easy, quick meal. Actually I use onions and garlic in a great many dishes I cook. Garlic, onions, and ginger root store well in a basket, especially a hanging wire basket because they require that air circulate around them to keep them from spoiling. You do not need wire or hanging baskets, however. If you have the space, a wicker basket that sits on the counter top will do as well if the wicker is not too tightly woven.

Bread Baking Center
Whole grain spelt flour
Whole wheat flour
Unbleached all-purpose wheat flour
Whole grain rye flour
Old-fashioned thick rolled oats
Buckwheat flour
Flaxseed meal
SAF Yeast
Bob's Red Mill Natural baking soda
Rumford Aluminum-Free baking powder

Baking bread is easy if you are organized. I have a small rolling cabinet whose top shelf holds the bread machine. An open shelf below holds my 25-pound sack of organic whole grain spelt flour. The bottom section, a cupboard with doors, is where I store flours that do not require refrigeration. Whole grain rye, buckwheat and flaxseed meal I refrigerate in hottest weather to keep their oils from going off taste. Extra flour I freeze to keep as fresh as possible. When not in use, this cabinet sits out of the way behind a screen. When I am ready to bake breads, cakes, pies, cookies, muffins or scones, I roll the cabinet over next to the kitchen counter where I measure and mix.

Much of the year I use the bread machine only for mixing and kneading the bread dough. I then shape the dough and let it rise in pans and bake in my gas oven. But two, sometimes three, months of the year when daytime temperatures exceed 100 degree F., I let the bread machine go full cycle and bake the bread. Flavor and texture are acceptable, but not as good as made in an oven. At least not in my bread machine. My machine does have a French bread setting, but all this seems to mean is that the second rising is ten minutes longer than the whole wheat setting.

On the subject of bread machines, I receive email asking which I recommend. I use an inexpensive model that I bought when my first much-loved bread machine wore out. I decided to buy this inexpensive one to use until I could do research and decide which one of the better models would best suit my needs and preferences.

In the meantime, by trial and error, I have developed ways of making good bread with this low-priced machine. For instance, I discovered that the "basic" setting actually bakes better whole wheat bread than the "whole wheat" setting, though I have no idea why this is so. The machine's basic setting bakes in 40 minutes less time than the setting designed for whole wheat. My conclusion is: if you just want good bread, it does not matter so much which brand of basic bread machine you buy. Just buy one and experiment until the bread tastes the way you want. Like many kinds of equipment, the skill of the user determines results more than the machine itself. It also helps to actually read the user manual. Sometimes following the directions can produce very good results.

If you have a food processor or a mixer with a dough hook, you do not need a bread machine. You can mix and knead your dough with your mixer or food processor and then bake in your oven. One note here: I understand that many of the food processors can only process dough for one small loaf at a time. Again, read your user manual so you won't find yourself cleaning out a great glob of dough from a machine that could not cope.

When my elderly toaster oven finally wore out, I replaced it with an electric counter top toaster/convection oven and experimented baking breads, scones, cakes and cookies in it. On really hot days, I put this little oven on my back patio to avoid heating up the kitchen. Claims are that convection cooks in less time than a regular gas or electric oven. I did not find this always true for my oven. Baking cakes and breads took about the same amount time or longer. But I did find that meats and fish did seem to cook in less time than in a regular gas or electric oven.

But the bottom line was that I really *do not like* the results of a convection oven as well as the old style toaster oven. Convection ovens do not make satisfactory toast. When a local charity asked for donations of household appliances, I presented them with the toaster/convection oven and bought myself a toaster/bake oven.

Now I can make *good* toast. Hooray.

Often I use organic, stone ground flours. Currently I bake most of my bread from organic whole grain spelt flour. I like the taste and texture of spelt bread better than wheat bread. While I have never been diagnosed with either wheat allergy or gluten intolerance, my digestive system seems happier when I avoid wheat. Like many people, I find it easier to stay slim when I keep my wheat consumption minimal.

Spice Shelf

Spices (dried): thyme, oregano, basil, dill, marjoram, savory, cinnamon, ginger, nutmeg, cloves, bay leaves, sage, turmeric, cumin, coriander, allspice, curry powder, garam masala, paprika, white pepper, whole black peppercorns, California red pepper flakes, caraway seeds, chervil, tarragon, chili powder, and Mediterranean sea salt

In my garden, I have a section devoted to herbs. The drought has taken its toll on my poor herbs. The oregano has survived, but the thyme is struggling. The sage, rosemary, and mint perished. (But a kind neighbor brought me a start of her drought-hardy mint that is producing well.) I always buy new basil for the pot on the back patio each spring.

Many Americans today ignore spices and herbs and depend on salt and sugar to give their foods flavor. But salt and sugar are two ingredients doctors and nutritionists tell us to limit for good health and weight control. French cuisine employs a moderate amount of salt and sugar, and French cuisine uses a variety of herbs and spices to give dishes wonderful taste. Herb gardens and herbs grown in pots are part of most French households. French markets sell fresh and dried herbs. The French also gather herbs that grow wild. Using herbs and spices to flavor foods help chic French women stay slim.

Growing herbs is an economical way to add wonderful flavor to whatever you prepare. Herbs can add attractive foliage and blooms to flower beds, even when you have no formal herb garden. Patio pots of herbs can make you think you are living in the south of France.

If many Americans do not regularly use herbs and spices in their cooking, there may be good reason. Americans are unlikely to grow or gather their own herbs, and those bottled and packaged versions supermarkets sell can be anemic. They won't give the flavor of better quality herbs and spices.

A source for quality dried herbs that I have found in the USA is Penzey's Spices. The company has a wonderful catalog in both magazine and online version. Reading their product descriptions is an education in the history and use of spices. If you are interested in learning more about herbs and spices, stick one of their catalogs in your purse or briefcase and pull it out and read it when you are waiting online or on hold.

I have been exceptionally pleased with the quality of the Penzey's individual spices I have ordered. I have not liked *any* of the Penzey's blends that I have tried.

My suggestion is that if you buy Penzey's excellent spices, that you order individual spices and mix your own spice blends. Recipes for these blends are easy to find on websites and in cookbooks. If you wish to try blends Penzey's offers, first order the sample size. Then, if you do not care for the taste, you can discard or give away the blend without too much money wasted. Mixing you own spice blends can fine tune a blend to your taste. For making *herbes de Provence*, I follow the recipe of Simone Beck, who along with Julia Child, was one of the three authors of the original *Mastering the Art of French Cooking*. The Frenchwoman's recipe is easy to remember as MOTTS. You mix one part marjoram, one part oregano, two parts thyme, and one part savory.

Growing garlic is easy. Though whether you plant in spring or fall depends on the geographic area in which you live. There are many varieties of garlic, each with a subtle difference in taste. You can cook with green garlic, as well as with the mature bulbs. If you find that garlic you bought at the store is sprouting, plant it. Farms specializing in gourmet garlic sell plants. You can locate them using an Internet search engine. Garlic plants are also sold by nurseries and seed catalogs.

Tea Chest
Assam
Darjeeling
Earl Grey
Earl Grey decaf
Steamed Green Darjeeling
Yorkshire Gold
PG Tips
English Breakfast
English Breakfast decaf
Irish Breakfast decaf
Rooibos, green
Rooibos, red
Chamomile
Peppermint
Tea biscuits

When I write tea chest, the words bring to mind a wooden chest with brass fittings and hinges, surely oriental in style, and inside small compartments for various teas to be stored. I wish I owned such a chest. Instead I have a handy section of my cupboard devoted to my assortment of teas and the canisters in which those teas are stored.

Tea must be protected from heat, air and light to preserve quality and flavor. The general rule is that green teas will retain their flavor for six months if stored properly. Black teas can be stored for a year under proper conditions. Metal canisters have long been preferred for tea storage. Plastic can distort the taste. Glass lets in damaging light. Most tea merchants offer a selection of metal tea cannisters also called tea tins—from the utilitarian to the truly delightful. Some teas are sold packaged in metal containers that can be reused.

If you go into a tea shop and they store their tea in clear glass jars, walk out. These shopkeepers do not know the most basic fact about tea, and you will be buying a damaged product, even if the quality of the tea leaves that was put in those clear glass jars was excellent.

Generally, loose teas are superior in taste to bagged teas. Loose teas, in addition to better quality, offer you greater control over brewed strength and quantity brewed. And many teas are beautiful to watch unfurl as they brew. A glass teapot lets you watch this unfurling.

These days I am drinking more teas that come packaged in tea bags. The convenience, particularly in the morning, of dropping a tea bag into the warmed teapot and pouring on boiling water saves finding the measuring spoon and the tea infuser and measuring the loose tea into the infuser.

Also the two teas that I most regularly drink for breakfast, Taylors of Harrogate Yorkshire Gold and the popular PG Tips (in tea pyramids), are excellent quality bagged teas. In a decaf tea, English Tea Store's Irish Breakfast Tea Decaf in teabags is one of my favorite decaf teas. But I find the Tea Store's loose version of Irish Breakfast Tea Decaf undrinkable.

I keep a few teabags in my purse because the quality of tea offered in many restaurants in the USA is grim. Also, many American homes are so devoted to coffee that you may find all they can offer tea drinking guests is vile instant tea. In this case, it is BYOT, Bring Your Own Tea.

Various tea merchants sell packages of fillable teabags, actually tea sacks, that you can fill with your own loose teas and take them with you.

I use the t-sac brand. The sacks are chlorine free and made in Germany. Green teas have an advantage as take-with-you teas. Black teas must steep in water brought to rolling boil and poured immediately over the tea. But green teas steep in hot water, about all you can hope for when ordering tea in restaurants in the USA. I order a cup of tea with "teabag at the side" and substitute my own teabag if the quality of the provided teabag is unacceptable.

When I wrote the original version of this book I was often drinking rooibos tea, both red and green rooibos—though to my taste buds green rooibos tastes more like regular tea than the red version of this South African caffeine-free tea.

Some claims of health benefits for rooibos have been exaggerated, especially concerning the amount of calcium and magnesium in a cup of this tea. Yet, of the non-caffeine teas, rooibos has an advantage over decaf teas and some herbals. Because of its low level of tannins, it is believed to interfere less with the body's absorption of iron.

Several years ago, when I was seeking solutions to a problem with fatigue I was experiencing, I cut back on regular tea and substituted herbal teas, chiefly chamomile and peppermint, two favorites. Then I read that tests had shown that these two herbal teas, while caffeine-free, interfered with iron absorption almost as much as regular tea. So I switched to drinking rooibos tea with iron-rich foods, and found an improvement in my energy level. (I also increased my consumption of potassium-rich foods, it should be noted.) I still drink chamomile tea, long believed beneficial for skin. I also drink peppermint tea, a digestive aid. But I drink chamomile and peppermint teas when I am not eating foods high in iron. By the way, tannins, I understand, only interfere with non-meat iron. So you could sip your regular tea with your liver pâté tea sandwiches without concern, I assume.

Americans do not readily associate afternoon tea with the French, though the custom is popular there and often referred to as *thé de cinq heures*, five o'clock tea. Tea is a perfect beverage to pair with those wonderful French *pâtisseries*, and late afternoon a wonderful time of day to indulge. France has a number of elegant tea salons in which to take afternoon tea. I have received email from *Chic & Slim* Women telling of their lovely experiences taking tea at *Mariage Frères*, or in other equally delightful French tea salons.

When I include tea biscuits on the tea chest list, I mean biscuits in the sense of the French *biscuits*, what in the USA we call cookies. Most cookies made in the USA contain too much high fructose corn syrup and chemicals to be acceptable to me. But I have located several cookies for sale in my supermarkets that are baked by European, Canadian and UK companies, as well as some healthier domestic cookies health food that have acceptable ingredients and are sufficiently elegant that they are a chic addition to teatime. Some of my favorites are Newman's Own Fig Newmans, LU Rich Tea Biscuits, Voortman Sugar Free Mocha Cappuccino Wafers and, of course, Walkers Pure Butter Shortbread. I adore Scotch shortbread.

Fruit Bowl

1 or 2 kinds of fruit, varies by season

Most fruit that I buy needs home-ripening. I do keep fruit in my refrigerator, but I do not put it there until it is properly ripened. Until ripe, pears, peaches, apples, bananas and such sit in my pewter fruit bowl. An exception is grapes. I find grapes need to ripen in the refrigerator, else they spoil. Sometimes it takes two weeks after purchase to bring grapes to their peak taste. Another exception is Texas-grown citrus that is usually at peak for eating when it arrives in my stores.

EMERGENCY RATIONS IN THE SLIM PANTRY

The realities of the world in which we live today makes keeping a slim pantry somewhat more complicated than previously. Is the idea of emergency rations compatible with that of a Slim Pantry? Should emergency rations be kept separately from Slim Pantry items? Which Slim Pantry basics as previously noted would serve as good emergency rations? We need to consider these questions and their answers if we are going to make the Slim Pantry Technique work well for us.

Preparedness has great value. If you are prepared, you will more likely survive an emergency. And surely you will survive with much less discomfort than if you are not prepared. In my life, having gone through several tornadoes, a war, a political insurrection, and numerous African *coups d'etat*, I can assure you that when you are prepared, an emergency, while having its uncertain and uncomfortable moments, can even be an exciting adventure.

An important value of being prepared is that it can keep you out of the paralyzing and damaging grip of fear of something that may, or may not, happen sometime in the future. President Franklin Roosevelt told the American people in the dark days of World War II that all they had to fear was fear itself. But, as Thomas Friedman wrote in his 2005 national bestseller *The World Is Flat*:

"One of the most dangerous things that has happened to America since 9/11, under the Bush administration, is that we have gone from exporting hope to exporting fear. We have gone from trying to coax the best out of the world to snarling at it way too often. And when you export fears, you end up importing everyone else's fears."

Since 9/11 we Americans have allowed ourselves to become a nation afraid. Our fears have facilitated negative consequences to our lives. The best defense against negative consequences is intelligent preparedness. When I was growing up in Tornado Alley, that region of the USA that often experiences storms that take a high toll of property and lives, we did not live in fear. We were prepared. We had storm cellars and warning systems. Families had routines for what to do when the warnings came.

In addition to the threat of tornadoes, I also grew up, as everyone in 1950s America did, with the threat of nuclear attack. For that possible Cold War calamity, preparedness also served as an antidote to fear. Periodically our school day was enlivened with Civil Defense drills in which we children were required to dive under our desks and cover our heads with our hands. This activity always depressed me. Given my avoirdupois, I had trouble fitting *in* a school desk. Only a percentage of me could be squeezed *under* a desk.

Many families, in an effort to be good citizens, actually stocked their storm cellars with water purification pills and canned foods. These canned items, however, tended to be those for which there was not room in the kitchen pantry, usually home-canned peaches, green beans, and a green tomato relish we called "chow chow". Not the most complete survival fare.

My teenage years I was the regular babysitter for the only family in the area known to have a built an according-to-the-Civil-Defense-manual bomb shelter and stocked it with a year's supply of canned food. I took comfort in the thought that, if a nuclear attack were launched while I was babysitting, I would be in the local location that offered the best chance of survival. On the other hand, I realized that would also mean that I would be cooped up indefinitely in one small underground room with three preschool age children and a large quantity of Dinty Moore Beef Stew. This realization may have been a factor in developing my strong preference for diplomacy instead of war for settling conflicts.

Today we must prepare for terrorist attacks and natural calamities that seem to be growing ever more destructive despite our sophisticated warning systems. Though many of us live in areas where the risk of terrorist attack is reasonably low, every area is at risk for phenomenon that can knock out utilities or make going out to buy food difficult. Water mains can break and take days to repair and restore service. We need bottled water and emergency food for those times. A supply of take-with-you food is needed for evacuations.

How much food should you stock for an emergency?

At the time of Hurricane Katrina in August 2005, Pam Stegner, a preparedness advocate in Missouri received media attention for her home stockpile of emergency rations. The article I read stated that for her family of five, Pam Stegner has a gravity-fed water purifier able to process 30 gallons of water a day. She has stored 600 pounds of rice and beans, 18,000 dried eggs, and 16 tons (!!) of organically grown hard winter wheat. The photograph accompanying the article showed large cans of vegetable garden seeds one assumes could be planted to provide fresh vegetables.

Shortly after Hurricane Katrina, Sally Quinn writing in the *Washington Post* discussed the need to stockpile food for an emergency. Her article quotes Stephen Flynn, a terrorism expert at the Council on Foreign Relations, who believes dirty bombs and assaults on chemical facilities near large population centers and on the food supply, will be the next likely forms of terrorism. Because an attack on the food supply is a possibility, it becomes especially important that you stock food.

What emergency foods you stock will be determined by what is available, your food preferences, and any special food needs of your family, especially special dietary requirements for food allergies or health conditions such as heart problems or diabetes.

Your emergency rations must also include food and water for your pets. The most important item on my emergency supply list is drinking water. The second most important is cat food. With finicky cats that show zero tolerance for even the most temporary interruptions to their food preferences, I would not risk adding their displeasure to my disaster discomfort.

One emergency preparedness article I read not long after Hurricane Katrina stuck the Gulf Coast recommended feeding a brand of pet food that your pet did not particularly like during the emergency. Ridiculous idea! Obviously the person who suggested that knew little about dogs and cats. A disaster or an evacuation will be traumatic enough for your pet. You want to keep as much familiar and normal as you can. That certainly means sticking with your pet's regular brand of pet food, if possible. Also a change in diet can sometimes cause intestinal distress. Do you really want to risk adding a pet with diarrhea to your disaster problems?

The decade that I lived on the Gulf Coast, at the beginning of each hurricane season, long before any tropical storm began brewing in the Atlantic, I would buy six cans of tuna, six cans of vegetable juice, a package of crackers (in case my home-baked bread supply was low when a hurricane threatened), three power bars, and several gallon bottles of spring water. I stowed these items in a special section of my cupboard. With the food that I normally kept on hand, these would see me through a storm, at least until utilities were restored and life became reasonably normal.

Whatever amount of whatever foods and beverages you stockpile for emergencies, there will be less temptation to snack on them when hungry if you store them separately from your Slim Pantry items.

If you really think you might tear into that dark chocolate some midnight when you are watching television and have an attack of the munchies, you might even want to keep emergency rations in a container that has been closed with sealing tape and stowed in the back of the closet. Those inexpensive plastic tubs with tight fitting lids are recommended for storing emergency supplies. They have an advantage over cardboard boxes that they will float—if not too heavily loaded.

As you organize your Slim Pantry, do give attention to your emergency ration supply. And do it soon.

SLIM PANTRY FOR A SLIM BODY

French women gain such wonderful benefits from keeping a limited amount of food in their kitchens pantries.

Taking the time to Clean Out for Slim and then to Stock for Slim will bring you those healthy and slimming benefits that chic French women enjoy from their own kitchen and pantry organization.

Chic & Slim Savvy

Smart Thinking for Chic & Slim

Chic French women are savvy about making their lives happy, pleasure-filled and successful. || Some American women, though intelligent and well-educated, often are not savvy in the way they set about working toward their life goals. || **This technique is designed to help you develop chic French savvy so that you can have a life that is happy, pleasure-filled and successful. And that you can be chic and slim.**

IT'S A SPECIAL KIND OF INTELLIGENCE. Savvy is a variety of smart that is well-informed and perceptive. Savvy sees beneath surface appearances and deceptions. Savvy carries a kind of shrewdness that gives an edge. Easy to see the connection between savvy and the French verb *savoir*, to know. *Savoir faire* means knowing how to do something the right way that achieves your goal. Being savvy is more useful for a woman than just having a high IQ—or a number of impressive university degrees.

We all know people with their Phi Beta Kappa key dangling from their keychain and their Mensa cards tucked in their wallet who make the most atrocious financial and relationship choices. Some of them also fail dismally in the personal style department.

They may be highly intelligent, but they are not savvy.

Chic French women impressed me with their savvy. What exhilaration I felt when I realized that French women could express intelligent opinions and engage in serious conversations, have a life that employed their intelligence, yet not pay a penalty for it. Wow! I felt as if a weight had been lifted. As if I had shed twenty pounds and learned to dance the tango all in one night. As if an avenue had opened up before me that would lead to all sorts of possibilities and pleasures of being both smart and chic.

I made this discovery in the 1960s. In the USA in those days, women needed to hide their intelligence with silence, with playing dumb, and with wide-eyed naiveté.

Women whose intelligence was obvious, or who achieved success in their careers, often had to pay social consequences. Yet, while French women did not hide their intelligence, neither did they flaunt it. For their intelligence, as for their cleavage, French women know how much to reveal—and when and how to reveal it—to their maximum advantage.

THE SALONISTES

Later, after I began to investigate why French women possess an ability to meld intelligence and chic to a greater extent than American women—and apparently more than women of many other nationalities as well—the credit seemed to go to women we now call the Salonistes.

These women from the 17th century on into modern times invited to their homes the most intelligent writers and thinkers of their day for literary and political discussions and social amusements.

In his March 2005 article in *The New York Times* titled "Women who Conquered Europe With Their Wit" Jeremy Eichler described salons:

"They were places where ideas could be debated, new art, literature and music were consumed, and spirited discussion of politics could take place free of the influence of the court. And since a charming hostess was at the heart of just about every salon, the gatherings have also been seen as islands of proto-feminism, places where exceptional women could advance their private ambitions at a time when they were largely blocked from public life."

CATHERINE DE VIVONNE

The remarkable (and certainly savvy) 17th century woman who originated and gave the distinctive character to the French salon was Catherine de Vivonne, Marquise de Rambouillet.

Not only did the marquise establish and popularize by example this new social institution that had considerable influence on the French language and literature, she was a one-woman lifestyle revolution. Catherine de Vivonne set the precedents that changed the way the French designed the interior space and decorated their houses.

Catherine de Vivonne also refined and civilized social behavior. *The Cambridge History of English and American Literature* notes: "When Madame de Rambouillet brought together in her salon the most cultured men and the most beautiful women in France, she created a new standard of social refinement for Europe. The management of intimate relations between the two sexes became a proof of good breeding, and the degree of civility in any court could almost be measured by the influence which ladies enjoyed in it."

Though she lived four centuries previously, Catherine leaves us lessons that savvy women can put to good use today. A look at her life helps us learn those useful lessons.

Catherine de Vivonne was born in 1588 in the Rome of the Italian Renaissance. Her mother was Italian of the aristocratic Savelli family that traced descent from the Strozzi and Medici families. Her father, the Marquis de Pisani, was the French Ambassador. At age 16, this young woman of French and Italian parentage was married to the French Count d'Angennes who later became Marquis de Rambouillet.

Catherine and her husband set up their household in Paris. The new bride was not at all pleased with her life in France. To her, the gross manners of Henry IV's court were repulsive. Having grown up in sunny Italy, Catherine found the big, drafty French houses perpetually chilly in gray and damp Paris.

Catherine had inherited a large house on the Rue Saint-Thomas du

Louvre (unfortunately demolished in a later century to make way for extended palace gardens). She had the house rebuilt to her design. Smaller, cozier rooms placed within larger ones, some elevated and reached by an adjacent staircase were an innovation. She brought the windows down to the floor, enlarging them to allow in maximum light. To create views from the windows, she planted trees and designed flower beds in interesting arrangements. She hung pictures and installed plenty of chairs. Pictures on the walls and chairs to sit on seem basic to us today. But in Catherine's era, they were innovations.

Her *pièce de résistance* was her famous blue reception room, her *Chambre Bleue* where she received guests while cozily ensconced in her bed. Catherine suffered an illness that invalided her for several years. She designed her Blue Chamber so that, despite being confined to bed, she could still enjoy the company of visitors. Catherine's home was elegant, orderly, and comfortable. To this home she invited leading artists and writers and military officers—and the most brilliant and witty women.

THEIR THIRST TO LEARN

At this time, the Renaissance was lifting Europe out of the "dark ages" of wars and superstition. Women were reading, but they were doing their reading "shut up in their *châteaux*." They were also experiencing what one authority on the French salons termed *leur soif de savoir*, their thirst to know. They wanted to participate in the exciting intellectual life blooming around them. Catherine de Vivonne created an ingenious way for women to learn and to participate in a rich intellectual life that is still paying dividends for French women today.

Amelia Gere Mason in her book *The Women of the French Salons* made an astute observation that women who wanted a rich intellectual life but who shut themselves up in libraries and studied books learned only about *mankind*. But the women who participated in the salons learned about *men*.

The salons, with their mix of intelligent and witty people of both sexes, gave women not only academic knowledge, but also helped them better understand the male of the species and develop skills for amicable interaction with them. Over the years these skills have proved extremely useful for French women.

One difference between French and American women I have observed is that French women do not seem to join the equivalent of women's professional and social organizations common in the USA. I am talking about organizations whose meetings are almost invariably all-female in attendance. Most French women I knew had no interest in meetings attended only by women.

Catherine de Vivonne believed in the advantages of learning in a social situation that included both men and women. When she had been introduced to court life and found it disgusted her, she had secluded herself for a time and studied the classics. But there she was, living in Paris, one of the intellectual capitals of the world. Studying the classics in seclusion did not give her, nor other intelligent women like her, access to the brilliant writers and thinkers living in the city.

So Catherine devised her wonderful solution. She redesigned and redecorated her home to make it such a beautiful showcase of elegance and comfort that even the King and Queen copied her decorating ideas. Rigid protocol of the time determined who could attend court functions, but to her own home, Catherine could invite even those brilliant minds who were not aristocrats. In doing this, she circumvented customs that prohibited these intellectuals from other social circles. The beautiful women she invited to participate in her salons were not empty-headed pretties there as mere ornaments. They were intelligent women who were expected to participate in the salon with wit and charm. It would be a pleasure for brilliant men to be in their company.

Women who participated in these salons were expected to be agreeable, to articulate their ideas well, and to follow the rules of conversation. If the French have long excelled in intelligent social conversation, they owe a debt to that Italian-born Parisian hostess who set the guidelines and exerted her charm in persuading others to accept them.

NOT JUST A MUSE

The women attending Catherine's salons (and later salons) were there to participate, not merely to act as muses for the male participants— although they did often serve that purpose as well, it is true. For example, Catherine's beautiful daughter Julie d'Angennes inspired the *Guirlande de Julie*, a collection of 17th century French love poems written by her suitor to gain her hand in marriage. The Marquis de Montausier must have been a slow writer. By the time he finally finished the *Guirlande* and won her agreement to marriage, Julie was thirty-eight.

Catherine de Vivonne did not aim to create the French literary salon. Yet, in fact, she did.

Her initial objective had been for women to participate in French intellectual life in social gatherings that were conducted with good taste and civility. Catherine made the rules that demanded such proper behavior, and she, daughter of a French ambassador, had the tact and diplomacy to see that guests at her salons followed her rules.

Salons provided higher education for women during times when they were prohibited from attending universities. Catherine de Vivonne's salons were called a seminary for women authors because of the number of women writers who gained their education and verbal skills in this intellectual environment. By the time she died at age 94, one of them, Madeleine de Scudéry, had produced a large body of novels and other writing, among them persuasive arguments for the rights of women.

WHAT ABOUT THE HUSBANDS?

Throughout my study of Catherine de Vivonne, I was curious about the French husband of this woman who established her first salon around 1610 and continued her salons for more than three decades. What sort of man was he that gave his wife the freedom to create such intellectual opportunities for women? One clue came in a statement in an article *La Situation des Femmes et les Salons au XVIII Siècle*. (The Situation of Women and the Salons of the 18th Century.)

La Situation says: *"les maris sont libéraux, absents ou morts."* The husbands of the Salonistes were liberal, absent, or dead. My sources on Catherine de Vivonne contain little information about the Marquis de Rambouillet, although one source suggests he may, like Catherine's father, have been a diplomat. That would put him in the liberal or absent categories.

That Catherine was a woman about whom there was "never a word of scandal" and who produced seven children, seems to suggest that the Marquis was around for at least part of the time. So we must assume that the Marquis was liberal in supporting the development of the intellectual capacities of women, and willing to approve Catherine's expenditures on major remodeling and redecorating of their home in Paris, as well as the costs of entertaining for some thirty years.

CATHERINE DE VIVONNE'S SAVVY

Catherine was savvy in establishing intellectual discussion groups made up of both men and women, not just discussion groups for women. Because both sexes were included, French salons developed into social gatherings in which cultivated, intelligent women became true partners in discussions of religious, political, and scientific ideas. In turn, these women were capable of injecting a playfulness into these social gatherings. They made the intellectual discussions more fun for men than if the salons had been men-only.

If there exists in France more than in other countries, a social tradition of good rapport and of word play between the two sexes, in large part, it is due to this foundation established in the French salons. And if French women have been less enthusiastic about feminism than elsewhere, it is because French women are careful to avoid doing anything that might destroy this unique French harmony.

The second American president John Adams was most impressed by French women. In 1778, during that period when the new country was cultivating the aid of France in its struggle for independence, John Adams was sent to France to work with Benjamin Franklin and other Americans representatives there to negotiate that aid. His biographer

David McCullough writes in *John Adams*: "He enjoyed particularly the company of women of fashion whose animated opinions were as much a part of every social occasion as those of the men. In such company no gentlemen would be tolerated in monopolizing a conversation."

David McCullough also quotes from a letter John Adams wrote to his wife Abigail about French women: "To tell you the truth, I admire the ladies here. . . .They are handsome, and very well educated. Their accomplishments are exceedingly brilliant. And their knowledge of letters and arts, exceeds that of the English ladies, I believe."

SALONISTES AS MUSES

Some have overlooked the Salonistes' savvy self-interest in establishing their salons. They have ignored the benefits to the Salonistes and other women and have seen the feminine role as simply one of muse and facilitator. As Stuart Jeffries wrote in his 2005 *Guardian Unlimited* article that the salons "were seemingly hosted by moneyed and leisured women prepared to do what women don't want to do any more—help often self-obsessed, insecure men find their way and become geniuses." That said, the writer proceeds to describe the more important role of salons in educating women, as well as giving them a place to display their literary, musical and intellectual abilities.

But the Salonistes did often serve as muses. One French Saloniste remembered for that role is Geneviève Straus. Her first husband was Georges Bizet. The French composer died shortly after the 1875 premiere of his opera *Carmen*. Not long afterward, his widow remarried a wealthy lawyer Emile Straus.

While the husbands of earlier French Salonistes might have been defined as liberal, absent, or dead, Geneviève's husband wryly called himself the "senior valet" of the beautiful woman who was a prominent Saloniste of Belle Époque Paris. Her salons were frequented by Debussy, Degas, and Zola. One aspiring writer frequently in attendance was the young Marcel Proust to whom Geneviève Straus gave five slender notebooks in which he began the notes for his *À la recherche du temps perdu*. It was at Geneviève Straus' salons that Marcel Proust met Charles Haas on whom the writer would base his character of Swann. Geneviève herself provided the writer with his model for the unforgettable Duchess de Guermantes.

Salons spread from Paris. Women in London, Berlin, Vienna and other European cities also established vibrant and successful salons. Somehow the idea was not as well received on the American side of the Atlantic. Edith Wharton writing in *The Age of Innocence*, her vivid portrait of New York in the 1870s, wrote: "Medora Manson, in her prosperous days, had inaugurated a 'literary salon'; but it had soon died out owing to the reluctance of the literary to frequent it."

SALONISTES AS ROLE MODELS

Jacqueline Kennedy Onassis greatly admired the French Salonistes. She was reported to have taken as her role models Madame de Maintenon and Madame Récamier. Her choices, in view of her own life, are interesting. Both of these 18th century French Salonistes that Jackie admired so much were survivors.

The beautiful and intelligent Madame de Maintenon was known for her savvy insight into life and situations, as well as for her tranquility and diplomacy. As a young woman she was forced into a marriage with a deformed invalid. Later widowed, she became a governess to support herself and eventually was able to buy herself a marquisate and marry, in secret, French king Louis XIV.

The Duchess of Devonshire said of Madame Récamier that "First, she is good, then she is intellectual, and after this, she is very beautiful."

What a wonderful combination: good, intellectual, beautiful. Still, Napoleon banished Madame Récamier from Paris, as he did Madame de Staël, another brilliant Saloniste. The French Emperor saw these intelligent women as a threat, interesting considering the extent to which he was dependent on his wife Josephine for help and advice. (Though eventually, he banished Josephine too.) Napoleon was known for his unenlightened views on the place of women, as the laws he established, his Napoleonic Code, demonstrated. Stuart Jeffries sums up Napoleon's opinion of salons in a *Guardian Unlimited* article: "they were perverted institutions since they took women away from their roles as wives and mothers and brought them into contact with highly strung artistic types with anti-social ideas and fruity dress codes."

Despite his anti-Saloniste bias, Napoleon did later relent, and allow Madame Récamier to return to Paris and reestablish her salon there.

Jacqueline Kennedy Onassis may have most admired Madame de Maintenon and Madame Récamier, but Catherine de Vivonne was, in fact, the Saloniste whose accomplishments Jackie's seem most to parallel. As someone who remembers vividly the years of the Kennedy Administration, I find these similarities particularly striking.

While Catherine de Vivonne is credited with creating literary salons, her first project that so radically changed the design, decoration, and arrangement of French houses was the restoration of her residence, the Hotel de Rambouillet. Likewise, it was Jackie's restoration of the White House that launched an interest in renovation and decorating. Jackie devised glittering social occasions that set new (French) standards for food and entertaining in the USA. Her interest in history, literature, music and art made them chic. She made headlines inviting to the White House Nobel Prize winners and others of outstanding achievement in the arts and sciences. Like Catherine de Vivonne she always behaved in the most proper manner. I once read an account of an incident in which Jackie was in a meeting in New York City at the offices of a charity she supported. One of the charity's clients, an extremely intoxicated and odorous homeless man, barged into the meeting and presented himself to the former First Lady.

"How lovely to meet you," said Jackie.

Jacqueline Kennedy's intelligence was soon recognized by those who met the young First Lady. After a conversation with her, French president Charles de Gaulle told her husband President John Kennedy that she knew more French history than most French women. But in one major way, Jackie did not model herself on the French Salonistes. As a young woman she began camouflaging her keen intelligence speaking in a babyish voice and effecting a wide-eyed naiveté, although reportedly, Jackie was capable of speaking in a normal adult voice without affectations and was overheard doing so speaking French in Europe. Perhaps in a milieu where an attractive woman was not required to hide her intelligence, she felt the freedom to speak more naturally.

THEN THINGS CHANGED

As I wrote at the beginning of this chapter, I felt great liberation in a social milieu where the French system predominated and where intelligence in women was accepted. In fact, I found that this milieu was completely opposite that of 1960s in the USA. In social gatherings with the French, a woman who was not well read, who was not well informed about current events and the latest books and films, who could not express her opinions in an articulate manner and who did not take care of her appearance as well, was the one who found herself left out socially.

Meanwhile in the USA, influenced by the growing feminist movement, the situation regarding women and their expression of their intelligence began to change. But not necessarily for the better. American feminism began telling women that attention to appearance was enslaving, that men were the enemy, that equal rights must be demanded.

Many women began to dress in the sloppiest manner, refused to wear makeup, or shave legs and underarms. Some even declined to use deodorant. They cropped their hair mannishly or neglected it altogether. Haircolor was out. For someone like me, indoctrinated in the French system with the belief that intelligence and attractiveness made the optimum combination, all these efforts to appear as unattractive as possible made no sense at all. The vivid memory of these days and my bafflement came back to me when I received an email from a woman who had been reading *Chic & Slim*. She wrote that she was delighted to learn that being intelligent and successful did not mean that you had to end up looking like some "uncleansed creature from the Black Lagoon."

When the bras were burned, when makeup was no longer worn, legs no longer shaved, when the most utilitarian (and unflattering) clothing and shoes replaced chic little dresses, and when women decided that being liberated meant they could describe the minute details of difficulties with their monthly periods in mixed company, there was not much feminine mystique left. At least not feminine mystique of the French variety that the world finds so enthralling and that French women put to such excellent use in their own quest for happiness and success.

Now in early years of the 21st century, we observe many intelligent, successful women in the USA whose personal appearance is extremely chic and attractive. Still, some women continue to believe that a chic personal style is incompatible with the life of an intelligent woman. Virginia Postrel recounts in her book *The Substance of Style* an example in the feminist intellectual author Jane Smiley. The article illustrates how neglecting appearance has not accomplished for some intelligent women what they had hoped.

Until her early 40s Jane Smiley wore glasses and plain white cotton underwear, as well as a short, masculine hairdo. She never shaved legs and arms, never wore makeup. She demonstrated the idea held for some time in the USA that women must choose between intelligence and beauty, between mind and body, between substance and surface.

But Jane Smiley had a problem. "Her studied indifference to her appearance was sending unwanted signals and hiding important aspects of her personality. The man she was interested in didn't see her as a woman."

Well, *quelle surprise!*

"Jane Smiley fretted to her therapist, her therapist sent her to his colorist. She loved her blond hair and even said that she was nicer to her kids after she got the new hair color."

I find puzzling that any woman with sufficient intelligence to earn university degrees, hold university teaching positions and write prize-winning novels has to be told that men are going to be more interested in a woman with an attractive, feminine appearance. This is not exactly classified information.

Yet, apparently, some women believe that their intelligence should be enough to attract an intelligent man. And true, we all know many women who devote themselves so completely to their skin care, their wardrobe and their exercise regime that there is no time left to cultivate their minds. A conversation with them is likely to be dull, especially since many women totally focused on their appearance only want to talk about themselves. So some intelligent women fear that if they become sidetracked with personal maintenance, there will be no time for intellectual development. Chic French women find time for both.

Chic French women demonstrate that you can develop intellectual capacities—as well as a chic personal style. The two are perfectly compatible. In fact, intelligence can be an aid to beauty. In design guru Dr. Donald Norman's book *Emotional Design*, he points out that when we see something we find attractive, we are responding on a visceral level. It is a gut reaction.

But, he says, the reaction to something beautiful happens on the reflective level. We see beauty when we look below the surface. Our reaction to something we find beautiful comes from conscious reaction and experience. Our reaction to beauty requires knowledge.

Dr. Norman is talking about design of useful objects in his book, but his observation that attractiveness is surface-only, but that beauty goes deeper, applies to feminine personal style as well. Without intelligence to understand and develop one's unique style, one might be attractive. But to develop beauty, especially a beauty that endures after youth is past, requires intelligence and knowledge.

A GORGEOUS EXAMPLE

Attractiveness can be surface only, but beauty requires that there be something of value below the surface. This helps explain why women whose face and figure are far from perfect are often defined as beautiful. For example, we now know that at Sophia Loren's first screen test, she was told that she could never be a screen actress. Nose too long, mouth too big, hips too broad. Forget it, *cara!*

Subsequent screen tests were equally discouraging. As I read *Sophia: Living and Loving* by A. E. Hotchner, I was struck by the information that Carlo Ponti, who was directing Sophia Loren's budding career, accepted her refusal to shorten her nose and lose weight to reduce her hips. But when he began to put Sophia on the path to international stardom, he insisted she begin a reading program. If Sophia Loren was going to become an internationally-acclaimed beauty, there had to be something below the surface of this woman that the camera found difficult to film.

Sophia Loren's limited formal education ended not much beyond middle school in a small war-torn Italian town. Sophia said of her reading program: "I began to discover the treasures buried in those books by Chekhov and Tolstoy, Baudelaire and Stendhal, Shaw and Dickens. I started to keep a notebook in which I recorded sentences from those books which I found particularly enlightening. I have never stopped writing in that notebook." Her intelligence has grown in tandem with, and nurtured, her beauty. The most recent photo I have seen of Sophia shows her at 80. She is still glamorous and beautiful.

THE SAVVY LESSONS

So, now that we have looked at the Salonistes and other savvy women, what guidelines do they provide us for developing and using our own savvy for a happier and more successful life?

First of all, you cannot be savvy unless you are realistic. If you fool yourself about the true nature of people and situations in which you find yourself, if your perceptions are based on wishful thinking rather than on what actually is, you can never be savvy. French women's tendency to be brutally realistic about people (especially men) is the foundation for their savvy. Their willingness to be realistic also helps them achieve both chic and slimness.

Second, you are not born with savvy. You have to develop it. Developing savvy requires knowledge, both self-knowledge, as well as a whole arsenal of facts, both academic and practical. Ignorance is not bliss, as a fallacious old saying tries to convince us. In fact, ignorance can get you in a lot of trouble and make your life complicated and miserable. If you do not believe this, sign contracts without reading the fine print.

Knowledge is power. The more you know—about everything — the savvier you can be. You must make an effort to learn, not just by acquiring a formal education, earning degrees, but by learning all sorts of practical skills, becoming knowledgeable about all sorts of subjects.

You also must take time to evaluate information. People who are savvy do not believe everything they read or that someone else tells them. They seek facts for themselves and weigh them against other information. Savvy people remember that different people have different needs, tastes and abilities. What is right for one person quite often is not for another. Savvy people choose what is right for them and ignore the rest.

Another savvy lesson from the Salonistes is the value of learning in a group that includes both men and women. As the quotation earlier in this chapter stressed, in social situations, the women who participated in the salons not only acquired information about art, literature, and politics, but they also had an opportunity to learn about men. The salons also provided a situation in which men could be taught a few useful things about women—and about civility as well.

SAVVY METHOD

One fact that always strikes me when I read about Catherine de Vivonne and her salons concerns her method. Her aim was to provide a means by which women could satisfy their *soif de savoir,* their thirst to learn. But Catherine did not use her inheritance to found a university for women and hire professors to lecture to them and give them examinations. Instead she remodeled her home and gardens to be beautiful and comfortable, and to meet her own special needs. Hence her *Chambre Bleue.* She invited both men and women to intellectual gatherings that were of benefit to both male and female participants. Women acquired their educations. Men received inspiration and critique. Everybody had a very pleasant time.

Another savvy choice Catherine, and those who followed her example, made for gaining women more intellectual and social opportunities was that they avoided an adversarial Them (men) vs. Us (women) attitude. Charm and wit gained them more equality than accusations and demands.

Salonistes and those women for whom they provided role models were also savvy about using their feminine qualities to be accepted by the brilliant men they met in the salons. In the salon system Catherine de Vivonne devised and that evolved under other Salonistes, attractiveness was useful, but conversation ability was vital.

If women were to converse with intelligent men, first of all they must read, study and listen to educated discussions to develop ideas of their own. They must develop an ability to express themselves in a lucid, non-confrontational manner. But wit and a well-cared-for appearance were also necessary, they knew, if they wanted a man to listen as they expressed their intelligent opinions and ideas.

If feminists wailed when I suggested in a previous *Chic & Slim* book that women perfect the ability to pout as a means to better relationships, they surely will object now that I suggest that women make an attempt to look attractive and keep social conversations non-combative even when discussing serious subjects. Please note here that I am talking about social conversations. Professional situations may demand more aggressive and confrontational approaches, though an attractive appearance and charm will surely help in those situations too.

MAKING YOUR OWN OPPORTUNITIES

Still another lesson we can learn from the Salonistes is that if women desire a rich intellectual life, it may be necessary to create the ambience in which this life can thrive. Today, our social interactions little resemble the conduct in Henri IV's French court that so disgusted Catherine as a young bride. Yet today many women find their social activities do not give them the intellectual opportunities they desire. At gatherings to which they are invited, some people drink too much and become verbally combative, others are only trolling for bed partners. Bores monopolize the conversation, some only want to discuss the most trite and shallow subjects. Others are only trying to sell something. Some seek converts to their religious belief or donations to their cause.

To enjoy the social situations of the sort you wish, you may have to organize your own occasions, be selective in those you invite, and not be shy about defining the parameters for interaction.

DOMESTIC ARTS

In an article about salons in *The Village Voice*, Leslie Camhi wrote:

> Years ago, in the basement of Yale University's rare-book library, I stumbled upon two Louis XV armchairs that once belonged to Gertrude Stein. They were upholstered in needlepoint by Alice B. Toklas according to Picasso's designs. Those chairs long haunted me. They evoked . . . . a distinctly feminine savoir faire, a domestic sublime, redolent of the body and warm with conviviality. High culture in an armchair! Needlepoint and Picasso! Just sitting around, they seemed to suggest, in the right company, might be a form of art.

Of course in the Paris salons hosted by Gertrude Stein and her companion Alice B. Toklas, as in all the salons, guests were not just sitting around, they were sitting around talking.

Brilliant and creative people were sharing ideas, collecting ideas, gathering the raw material for works of art and literature and even for new political systems.

Those familiar with the Gertrude Stein and Alice B. Toklas story know that it was Alice who provided the homemaking skills. Beyond embroidering the upholstery, she was also the cook, and after Gertrude's death even authored two cookbooks. Domestic comfort served as an aid to art.

THE POWER OF CONVERSATION

The article in which the quote by Leslie Camhi appeared was a review of a 2005 exhibit at the Jewish Museum in New York *The Power of Conversation: Jewish Women and Their Salons.*

The exhibit focused on fourteen Jewish women who held salons from 17th century France to Southern California in the 1940s. These salons had much in common with other salons through the centuries. What all salons demonstrated was, as the title emphasizes, the power of conversation: the power of the verbal exchange of ideas in a relaxed, civilized atmosphere moderated by an intelligent and talented woman in her own home.

Reviews of *The Power of Conversation* exhibit provide interesting analysis of salons. Stuart Jeffries writing in his *Guardian Unlimited* article titled "Not Just A Place To Do Your Hair" raises the question of why, if there were both men and women present at the salons, why did they not degenerate into chit-chat about household matters (women) and business (men) that dominate many social occasions today? He answers this by quoting Emily D. Bilski and Emily Braun, the curators of *The Power of Conversation* exhibit. "If men dwelled on their business or their properties, and women on their clothes and their children, the collective dynamic would be lost."

Right. If that had happened, the gathering would not have been a salon. And why it did not happen was basically two reasons. First of all, the successful Salonistes were savvy women who were skillful in guiding their salons so as not to allow trivial conversations. Second, the invitation list for a salon was selective. Very selective. Often even spouses of those who participated in a salon were not allowed to attend if they did not meet the intellectual and artistic standards of that salon.

Also, that the salons were held in private homes allowed them to be as exclusive as the Saloniste chose. The successful Salonistes were intellectual monarchs who reigned supremely over their salons as their intellectual kingdoms.

SETTING BOUNDARIES

This matter of the exclusivity of the salons brings us to another trait we observe in those who are savvy: they wisely know that for a satisfying and successful life, they must set boundaries. These boundaries make it possible to spend time on important matters, not allow the hours of their day to be eaten up by activities without value and by those whose demands would waste their hours.

But today salons and the power of conversation they provided are now past. *Au contraire!* Salons, I would argue, have never been so extensive and so active as today. For what are online discussion groups, blogs, and social media such as Twitter but the 21st century manifestation of salons?

CHIC & SAVVY

French women are both chic and savvy. Women of any nationality can be chic and savvy too—when we follow the chic French example.

Be chic, be happy and successful. Certainly be savvy.

However beautiful, or valuable, or poetic may have been the feminine types of other nationalities, it is in France that we find the forerunners of the intelligent, self-poised, clear-sighted, independent modern woman.

Amelia Gere Mason
The Women Of The French Salons

Blasé for Chic & Slim

Nonchalance for Chic & Slim

French women devote effort and financial resources toward staying slim. For the most part, they achieve admirable results for their small efforts. || American women devote much effort and spend billions of dollars annually on weight control programs, treatments and products. For the most part, money spent does not achieve the long-term results they desire. || **This technique will examine ways Americans hamper their weight control efforts by trying too hard. It will demonstrate how developing a blasé French attitude toward weight loss can help you become and stay slim as those chic French women.**

IF YOU CANNOT LOSE THOSE extra pounds no matter how hard you try, it may be that you are trying *too* hard.

Trying too hard, becoming tense in your desperation to achieve your goal, can prevent success in weight loss, just as it can prevent success in careers, sports and relationships. If you cannot lose weight despite following all the rules of whatever method you are using, it will likely help you take a more blasé attitude toward the process.

If you become more relaxed and nonchalant about weight loss and weight control the way French women are, you are more likely to lose that unwanted fat and stay slim.

For some of you, it has been so easy. Within days of adopting the French-inspired *Chic & Slim* philosophy, you have begun to shed unwanted pounds and to improve your personal style. And you have kept on losing unwanted fat. You have found that more and more often people are noticing and complimenting you on your chic style. And, okay, you are getting some catty comments from tacky, competitive types who are just aquamarine with envy. But that comes with the territory, doesn't it?

But a few of you have reported, that it just has not worked.

You have eaten in the French manner and you have improved your personal style. You have come to a point where you have decided that even if you lived on a steady diet of baguettes, foie gras, and escargot, if you wore Chanel from your underpanties out to your hair clip, you still would not lose those extra 25 pounds.

If you and your health care professional have ruled out a health condition or side effects from medication preventing your weight loss, it may be that to succeed, you need to become more blasé about your approach to weight control.

DEFINING BLASÉ

Blasé is not a word you hear often in the USA. For one thing, for someone to be described as blasé requires that they possess a degree of sophistication and calm nonchalance. Sophistication is not a trait one generally associates with Americans. Most Americans are too uptight, stressed-out, and competitive to display anything vaguely resembling calm nonchalance.

Sometimes a person's blasé attitude manifests itself in a disinclination to become unduly worried or concerned because they have experienced the situation so many times that it no longer provokes anxiety or raises the adrenaline. For example, the first African *coup d'etat* I experienced (a mere seven days after I set foot on the continent) was a heady mix of exciting and terrifying. By the time I went through the second *coup d'etat* two months after the first, both the excitement and terror levels had dropped several degrees. Later there came a period in which about every four or five weeks, usually on a Sunday, we had another *coup*. I would not even disturb my husband's Sunday afternoon nap to tell him the government had been overthrown again. My attitude toward political upheavals had definitely become blasé.

The French put great importance on staying slim. They are known for employing a variety of methods and aids to keep their bodies healthy and attractive. But even when a new theory of weight loss is introduced, or when word circulates about the great results a new spa treatment can achieve, the French manage to keep a blasé attitude. They will see the new program or treatment as something that could be useful and that they might try. But you would be unlikely to see the kind of reaction that Americans give a new diet or weight loss program that they embrace as a religion sure to offer them the weight loss salvation they seek.

Several years ago, a woman who worked in a San Antonio natural foods store told me that during a time when high demand produced a shortage of Dr. Atkins meal replacement bars, some customers finding these bars unavailable would become visibly upset. Some became nearly hysterical. Others got tears in their eyes. Upset, hysterical and tears because a meal replacement bar is temporarily out of stock is not blasé.

Upset, hysterical, and tears are particularly not blasé because they fail to demonstrate the requisite sophistication a blasé attitude inevitably contains. A sophisticated person would know that their weight control success or failure did not depend on whether or not they were able to purchase a particular brand of diet aid bar this week or next.

Or ever.

SHE WAS DEFINITELY BLASÉ

The first time I actually heard someone I knew described as blasé was during my university years. A male graduate student in his mid-20s used the word to describe another student in one of his graduate seminars. The student, a woman, was not the typical female graduate student. In those days, at that university, it was unusual for any woman in her late 40s to return to college. Almost a quarter century had passed since this woman had earned her undergraduate degree. She had married, raised a family, and now, divorced with a generous settlement, she had decided to return to her alma mater for a masters degree program.

She dressed for classes, not as the other female students did, but more as if she were some student's well-to-do parent there for a conference with the Dean. She wore tailored wool skirts and jackets with classy wool sweaters in soft neutral shades—and her diamonds.

Her hair was cut in that short, face-framing coif favored by French women of a certain age. Her mid-heel pumps and handbag looked straight from Neiman Marcus. Her paper for taking notes was carried in an embossed leather folder.

The graduate seminar was a tough one, required for the degree, and taught by a professor known for the severity with which he graded. The other students in the seminar, all in their 20s or early 30s, were sweating the course. But not Ms. Back-to-School-in-her-Late-40s.

Even though she had not been in a college classroom since Carole Lombard was starring on the screen at the campus theater, her attitude toward the seminar was definitely blasé. She refused agonize because the subject matter and the professor were difficult. And she was doing very well in both the seminar and her other graduate level courses.

SABOTAGING SUCCESS

An excellent example of how people can sabotage success by trying too hard involves pregnancy. Today we have a number of sophisticated medical procedures and medications to aid couples who are having difficulty creating a child. Not many decades ago, for couples having such difficulty beginning families, medical science could not do much beyond encourage them to keep trying.

Again and again you saw the same thing happen. After years of trying to have a child, a couple would give up and adopt a baby. Barely would they get the little adopted bundle through the front door and bingo! the woman became pregnant. I lost count of the women who told me how they had struggled with a colicky infant while suffering tortures of morning sickness.

Stress and tension can prevent the human body from doing what it is designed to do. Medical studies have shown this to be true for shedding excess fat, as for conceiving a child. For this reason, in order to lose excess fat, it is often helpful to shift the primary focus away from weight loss to personal style.

Focusing on what you eat or do not eat is a diet. Diets are stressful. Putting your focus on personal style, on becoming more chic, as I suggest, removes stress and gives the body a better chance of achieving healthy weight. Since healthy eating is necessary for true attractiveness, focusing on a chic personal style prevents unhealthy starvation tactics and overeating tendencies, both which mar appearance. Focusing on a chic personal style, you are more likely to lose weight gradually and keep the excess fat off permanently.

CASE STUDY OF SABOTAGE

Americans believe more is better. Often this belief causes them to seize the basic theory behind a weight loss method and then do more of it than is required. In the process, they sabotage their weight loss efforts. In some cases, not only do they fail to lose weight, sometimes, they gain. As I was working on this technique, an email arrived that demonstrated how someone can overdo a basically good technique for weight loss and, as a result, fail to lose weight.

A young woman who lives in West Virginia wrote:

> I read all three books over a year ago when I originally bought your books and failed miserably at [losing weight]. I may have ate foods that a French woman would chose, but I ate A LOT of it. I had bread with butter at every meal, cheese at every meal, coffee all day long, etc, etc. Finally, after not seeing results, I reverted to my old ways of eating...fried and fast food.

Of course, in the first place, as she subsequently recognized, she had eaten the bread and cheese and drunk the coffee, but in *large* quantities, not in moderate French women portions. Nor did she eat in the French style. For example, the French butter their breakfast bread, but at other meals, bread is eaten without butter. Bread the French eat does not contain the chemicals, fats, and sugars of most American supermarket bread. French bread flour is higher in protein than most American bread flour. Lack of added ingredients and higher protein make French bread better for weight control.

As for coffee, the French drink a generous cup (sometimes bowl) of coffee with breakfast. But following the midday and evening meals, coffee is served in tiny demitasse cups that hold only a few swallows. In a café, the French may order a *café crème* and sip it slowly. (Though I understand that a *café crème* is only ordered before 11 AM. The French do not drink "coffee all day long" in the American manner. Nor do French cafés and restaurants serve coffee in those gigantic foam or paper cups American coffee companies sell their brewed coffee concoctions.

Another example of how Americans overdo a weight loss technique to the point of defeating its purpose involves the misconception that a "diet food" can be eaten in unlimited quantities without causing weight gain. When "low-fat" products came on the market, many people trying to lose weight said, "Oh, these are low-fat, I can eat all I want." They did eat all they wanted. They did not lose weight. Often they gained.

DON'T TALK, JUST DO IT

Sometimes Americans become so obsessive about following a weight control system they provoke a negative reaction from others. You frequently know when an American is following a particular weight control program. They talk about it. Too often they talk about so much that their friends or family want to stuff a chocolate-covered doughnut in their mouth to shut them up.

In the days when Weight Watchers was the hot new weight control program, two couples of my acquaintance, took a joint two-week road trip. One of the wives had recently enrolled in Weight Watchers and was extremely focused on, as well as talkative about, her program. Never mind that the foursome was on vacation visiting historic sites and natural wonders, all Mrs. Dieter could talk about was her program. Though the other three were not dieting, Mrs. Dieter insisted they only eat in establishments that could meet her program requirements. Table conversation was dominated by what she could eat and could not eat, how she tallied up her points. Wait staff was harangued with questions about the contents and preparation of dishes.

The two couples were on the homeward leg of the trip somewhere in the open spaces of West Texas. Mrs. Dieter's husband had, from long experience, simply tuned her out. The other male in the group, a man whose wife's sensible, moderate eating had kept her slim their entire married life, had not developed a similar ability. That hot afternoon on a long, monotonous stretch of highway, Mrs. Dieter began to expound on her diet. That was just too much the generally mild-mannered fellow. "If you say the words Weight Watchers one more time, I will put you out of the car and you will have to walk," he said. And he meant it.

Having no conversation topic other than your diet is not blasé. French women do not talk obsessively about what they are doing to stay slim. They just do it. And they stay slimmer than American women.

UH OH! IT'S THE PURITANS

Why do Americans overdo their weight loss efforts, even when this often means defeating those efforts, yet the French, with their more blasé attitude, succeed much more effortlessly?

The American attitude finds its roots in Puritanism. American Puritanism is rife with *thou shalts* and *thou shalt nots*. You must do this, you must not do that—in order to earn your reward.

Implicit in Puritanism is the belief that the more *thou shalts* that you do and the more *thou shalt nots* that you do not do, the greater your reward will be. So, given this Puritan heritage, it is not surprising that an American attempting to employ the French system of weight control would say, okay, if French women eat a lot of bread and are slim, then the more bread I eat, the slimmer I will become.

Sorry, it just does not work that way.

THE COMPETITIVENESS FACTOR

Americans extreme competitiveness also is a factor defeating weight loss. Debra is having success losing some unwanted pounds by cutting back on portion size and by replacing the two alcoholic mixed drinks she used to drink at weekend parties with a glass of wine that she sips slowly throughout the evening, as French women do.

Her friend Allison observes Debra's weight loss and decides that if cutting back on portion size and replacing mixed drinks with red wine is enabling Debra to lose weight, she Allison will do more and lose more.

She will beat Debra at her own game.

So Allison begins skipping lunch entirely. She gives up all alcohol. Afternoons her productivity at work suffers and she sometimes snaps at coworkers, but she does quickly lose five pounds. She stays with her program working toward a twelve pound loss. Yet very soon her sudden decrease in caloric intake is interpreted by her body as "famine." Her body, as it has been designed to do, starts fighting against the weight loss, maintaining her current weight with fewer calories than it previously required for that same weight. Allison finds her weight loss stalled. When, discouraged, she goes back to eating as she did previously, she gains back the six pounds she lost.

Debra, who has used a more moderate approach, keeps off those pounds she shed. Debra has maintained a more blasé about her weight loss efforts. She has enjoyed better success.

INADVERTENTLY BLASÉ

Sometimes Americans inadvertently become more blasé about their weight loss efforts with happy results. An example of this is a phenomena usually referred to as The European Syndrome. Here is how it works.

For 24/7, year after year, an American woman rigorously monitors her food intake, she regularly works out at the gym, she tries every new weight loss plan that comes along. But she never quite permanently banishes those stubborn 10 pounds. Then comes the day she takes her dream trip to Europe. Since this will be only two weeks out of her life, she decides that she will not monitor her food intake, she will eat and enjoy the good food available.

So she gives up the strenuous striving to lose weight and instead eats delicious meals offered in the European restaurants. For two weeks her primarily focus is diverted from weight control to all the interesting sights she is seeing and new experiences she is enjoying. Then, she arrives back in the USA, and surprise! She steps on the scales and finds that she is five pounds lighter than when she boarded the plane. She tells her friend that she can't understand what happened, "I ate all those fantastic meals and I lost weight." And the friend says, "I know. The same thing happened to me when I went to Europe."

TAKING AWAY THE STRESS FACTOR

Medical science has found that stress itself can cause people to gain weight, even when their caloric intake does not increase.

We always perform better when we are relaxed and calm. All of us have tasks we perform competently daily, almost without thought. But let a situation arise where we become stressed because someone is watching us, or because we feel time pressure, and quite often our efficiency plummets.

For example, every day for months you have stepped off the elevator, walked down the hall, put your key the lock and opened your door. No problem. But one evening you step off the elevator and there is this weirdo standing down at the end of the hall. For some reason you cannot get that key into your door lock no matter how hard you try. You may even drop the key.

GIVE UP THE TENSION, NOT THE TRYING

But a word of warning is necessary here. Becoming blasé about weight control means giving up the tension and desperation that is making it more difficult for you to achieve your goal. Becoming blasé does *not* mean that you go off on a tangent in the opposite direction. The following story illustrates what I mean.

On a visit to my family in the 1970s, my mother and I went shopping. My mother at the time was enrolled in Weight Watchers, and she said she wanted to stop at a store and buy dessert treats that were allowable on her program. It was an interesting little store, the exact likes of which I had never seen before, nor since. Everything for sale was a diet food, a diet book, or some sort of aid for dieting the American way. In addition to the commercial food items such as the frozen treats my mother purchased, there was a section in which, instead of offering the traditional American bakery items such high calorie sugared doughnuts, cinnamon rolls, cookies and such, it offered freshly-baked items that were all low-calorie, sugarless and low-fat diet versions baked by the owner herself.

Later, my mother told me that the woman who owned the store was a weight loss success story. She had enrolled in a diet program, lost over 100 pounds, and now she taught classes in weight loss. She had opened the store to make available to others the diet aids that she had used to lose weight.

A couple of years later, I was again visiting my mother, again out shopping, but this time my mother was not with me. I happened to pass the store where she had bought the frozen treats. I noted that the location of the diet center now housed a traditional American bakery. The window that on my last visit had displayed diet products was now filled with doughnuts, cinnamon rolls and sugary cookies.

Knowing that Americans spend billions of dollars each year on diet products, I imagined that the shop had been such a success that the woman had opened a larger store in another location. Later, I asked my mother where the woman who ran the diet center now operated her business. "Oh, she is there in the same location," my mother said. "She regained all the weight she lost. Now she has a regular bakery."

Swapping diet foods for doughnuts and cinnamon rolls is not blasé.

THE SOPHISTICATION FACTOR

Blasé is sophisticated. Being sophisticated means being experienced in the realities of the world. Illusions have been discarded. You understand how the world works and you act accordingly. Some Americans both cause their weight gain and fail in efforts to lose weight because of unsophisticated food preferences. Even pushing into middle age, they still prefer kid foods: the sugary, the very salty, the fried, the eaten-with-fingers food. In fact, they may have a definite hostility toward more sophisticated tastes, rejecting them as elitist. Most likely, these "elite" foods are lower in calories and higher in nutrition. Eating them may also require a knife and fork.

For those who have been living on a steady diet of pizza, tacos, hamburgers, carry-out fried chicken, canned soups, soft drinks, toaster tarts and ice cream bars, suddenly finding themselves in the world of French food can be a shock. French food will likely not meet their definition of "tasting good." They will find it difficult to appreciate the subtle flavors of poached fish or steamed green beans with a bit of butter and a squeeze of lemon juice. To their taste buds, a small bowl of tiny *fraise de bois* will not compare to the sliced frozen berries drowning in sugar that meets their definition of strawberries.

Accustomed as they are to super-sweet taste of carbonated soft drinks, they will have difficulty appreciating the acidic taste of a dry wine or the freshness of chilled mineral water. When their definition of cheese is processed cheese food with hydrogenated oils and modified food starch fillers added, they may not appreciate the creaminess of a *brie*. They may have trouble accepting the idea that, in some cheeses, mold is part of the cheese.

Becoming blasé about food in a way that will facilitate staying slim means discarding hostility against certain healthy foods because someone has labeled them elitist or some other term that carries a negative connotation for you.

Frankly, I think elitist food sounds rather enticing. A lot more tempting than the idea of hick food.

Look beyond advertising hype and trends to find the nutritionally sound. This will help you achieve your goal of a healthy, attractive weight. You may need to "sophisticate" your tastes. This process of revising your food tastes may require effort. If you have always eaten fish fried in batter and smothered in tartar sauce or ketchup, it may take months before you can begin to appreciate the taste of broiled or baked fish. And you may have to discover herbs and spices that compensate for the flavor provided by tartar sauce or ketchup.

If you have always eaten your vegetables overcooked and seasoned with bacon or salt pork as in common in some regions of the USA, steamed vegetables served lightly salted and tossed in a bit of butter or olive oil, or served raw without dip, may not taste good the first few times you try them.

You may have to learn to recognize quality fruits so that the ones you buy and eat without added sugar will taste as satisfying as fruit that has been heavily sugared. You may have to learn to recognize quality vegetables so that they will taste flavorful without adding great amounts of salty animal fat.

You can speed the sophistication of your own food tastes (and increase your chances of becoming slimmer in the process), if you make an effort to replace the kid foods you eat with more sophisticated ones. For instance, you may have always eaten potato chips or corn chips with your sandwich. Instead, make a more sophisticated choice of sliced raw vegetables to accompany your sandwich.

Eating out in fast food places, you may have to bring your own sliced zucchini or mini carrots in a plastic bag in your purse. Fortunately packages of raw vegetables ready-to-eat are now sold in supermarkets. These can help those who want to eat in a more sophisticated manner, but who lack the time to prepare and package raw veggies before they leave home.

While we are on the subject of sandwiches, they can be replaced with a more sophisticated salad and a small portion of bread to accompany. (French women are definitely more likely to order the salad with bread than a sandwich.) Replace soft drinks with more sophisticated mineral water with a squeeze of lemon. Even a glass of plain water with or without a squeeze of lemon or lime is an improvement over soft drinks. Try chilled rooibos or herbal teas sweetened with stevia. Replace desserts such as cakes, cookies or pie with one moderate-sized piece of well-riped fresh fruit.

I receive email from some women who tell of their success: finally shedding those last five or 10 pounds, or the loss of 35 or 40 or 55. But then, in among these, I receive another kind of success story. In these email, women write to say that, thanks to *Chic & Slim*, they came to the realization that the goal they had been torturing themselves for years to achieve, that size 4 or size 2, was unrealistic. It was unrealistic for their body build and lifestyle when they were young, and it was truly unrealistic now that they are in their middle years with career and family demands that often make total control over food choices impossible.

They write that they have come to the conclusion that with their height and bone structure that their body was resisting being the willowy silhouette that had long been their dream. They had settled at a healthy, well-toned size 8 or 10 and were enjoying life so much more. One of them sends me the most marvelous descriptions of dinner parties and meals enjoyed in her area's fabulous restaurants. Some send me photos. And these women look marvelous at their realistic weight. Remember French women often weigh more than you think they do because of the clever personal style they have designed for themselves. Becoming blasé about weight control may mean becoming more realistic about what is the proper healthy weight for you.

Becoming blasé about weight control also means becoming sufficiently realistic to give up the fantasy of a miracle weight loss solution becoming available in the immediate future.

BECOMING REALISTIC, BECOMING SLIM

So many Americans have simply not given up hope that medical science will, sometime very soon, devise a pill or a laser beam or some combination of foods (eaten in the dark of the moon perhaps?) that will make it possible for them to have a perfectly slim body without making any lifestyle changes.

They want to be sedentary and overeat, yet be svelte or petite.

This undying hope for miracle weight loss becomes evident to me again and again in conversations that I have with people who have long struggled with excess weight as well as in writings of authorities on the topic.

Yet you cannot blame Americans for harboring miracle weight loss hope. In my own lifetime I have seen astounding achievements in medical science. When I was a child, polio killed, crippled and confined to an iron lung or wheel chair both adults and children. Then a polio vaccine was invented. They lined us up in the elementary school auditorium and gave us an injection. In a year or so, a new, better vaccine was created, this one administered as painlessly as possible: on a sugar cube that dissolved sweetly in the mouth.

In my lifetime, we have found treatments and cures for many illnesses that plagued humans for millennium. Who can blame some Americans for believing that next week, or next month or next year that medical science will give us the miracle treatment to let them overeat and never exercise, yet be the perfect healthy, attractive weight they desire? We know many researchers are working hard to find that miracle cure. The incentive is high. Whoever discovers a means to the perfect body that does not require changing eating or exercise habits has the possibility of becoming very, very, very rich.

In the meantime the obesity epidemic rages on. And many women keep losing and regaining that same fifteen pounds over and over and over.

So if you want your body in that slim silhouette you envision anytime soon, it will help greatly if you become more realistic. But for many this is not easy. Women particularly cherish the idea that someone, a knight in shining armor or a fairy godmother, will suddenly appear and make everything easy and wonderful for them.

But I tell you this:

> If you see yourself
> as a chubby Cinderella (*Cendrillon La Grande*)
> and still cling to the hope
> that one day the Fairy Godmother (*Marraine Fée*)
> will waive her magic wand over you
> and you will suddenly be Size 2 (*très petite*).
> Or, if you are gambling that soon a
> Knight in Shining Armor (*Chevalier à Armure Brillant*)
> will ride in on a white charger (*cheval blanc*)
> and slay the Fat Monster (*Le Monstre de Gras*)
> that keeps padding out your jeans,
> I have bad news.
> I don't think they are coming.

Becoming sophisticated, realistic, and most of all, becoming blasé, relaxed and nonchalant about weight control the way French women are, will more likely bring you the chic and slim results you desire.

Be blasé, be slim.

Success Resources for
Armoire Boudoir Cuisine & Savvy

Most of the background sources mentioned in this book are available for sale online, either new or used. Almost all are worth reading in their entirety. One exception is Gaston Bachelard's book *The Poetics of Space*. This is the sort of book you read in graduate school because it is required—but not otherwise. Michael Pollan's book *A Place of My Own* quotes and comments extensively on the French philosopher's book, however. And Michael Pollan's book is very entertaining.

Christa Weil's *Second Hand Chic: Finding Fabulous Fashion at Consignment, Vintage, and Thrift Stores* provides the sort of information French women learn growing up in a culture that reveres and demands quality.

The Women Of The French Salons By Amelia Gere Mason is available on *gutenberg.org*. Free versions in plain text, html, ePub or Kindle.

The two definitive works on Catherine de Vivonne, her salons and her decor innovations, are *Madame de Rambouillet ou la magicienne de la Chambre bleue* by Nicole Aronson and *Madame de Rambouillet's Chambre Bleue: Birthplace Of Salon Culture* by Jane Rather Thiébaud.

Nicole Aronson who passed away in 2010 was a specialist in women of 17th century France and a professor of French at several universities in the USA. Her book published by Fayard is available only in French.

Jane Rather Thiébaud's work on Madame de Rambouillet, the result of years of research, is the best and most comprehensive work in English. I have enjoyed delightful correspondence with Jane Thiébaud about that research. Unfortunately, The University of Maine currently restricts the online PDF of Jane Thiébaud's dissertation on Madame de Rambouillet to students and faculty.

About the Author
Anne Barone

Author Anne Barone is an independent writer and designer specializing in helping women dress chic, stay slim—and live happily and successfully. Since 1997, in her *Chic & Slim* books, and on her companion website to the books *annebarone.com* she has been sharing her translation of French techniques for dressing chic and staying slim — techniques that work for you no matter where you live.

Anne Barone lives in Texas where she is attempting to create a bit of French Provence, her *Provence-sur-la-Prairie*, on the North Texas plains. "Far enough in the country to grow eggplant, apricots and lavender. But close enough to Dallas to make the sales at Neiman Marcus."

Chic & Slim Books in Print and eBook